Treasury of
BARBIE® DOLL ACCESSORIES
1961-1995
by Rebecca Ann Rupp

Row 1: *Knitting for BARBIE®*, *BARBIE® and Ken™ Cut-Outs*, *BARBIE® Sings!*, Dell Comic Magazine *BARBIE® and Ken™*, *Skipper™ Doll Case*. Row 2: *BARBIE® 30th Anniversary Commemorative Silver Medallion*, *Twinkle Lite BARBIE™ doll –
McDonald®'s figurine*, *BARBIE™ and the Sensations™ – Rockin' Back to Earth* video, *Enesco® Promotional Button*, *Fossil Watch
– Pretty and Pink™*, *BARBIE® A Little Golden Book*. Row 3: *Deput 1959 BARBIE® – Hallmark Keepsake Ornament*, *Holiday
BARBIE® #1 – Hallmark*, *Montgomery Ward BARBIE™ doll* 1972 exclusive, *Peter Brams Designs – Nostalgic BARBIE™ Charm
Bracelet* in sterling silver. Row 4: *Mattel, Inc. 1994 BARBIE® 35th Anniversary – BARBIE™ Festival Pin*, Mattel, Inc. Plastic Strip
Display *"I'm Into BARBIE™"*, *BARBIE® Action Accents* Stereo, *Fluff™ Kitten*, *BARBIE® Electronic Piano*, *Angel Face BARBIE™
doll* wearing *Collector Series II – Springtime Magic*, *1959 - 1984 25th Anniversary BARBIE™ China Service*.

. Published by Hobby House Press, Inc.
Grantsville, Maryland 21536

DEDICATION

To my wonderful parents, thank you both for your love and support; also for encouraging me to have wings that enabled the pursuit of my dreams. Thank you both for giving me my first BARBIE® doll when I was four.

ACKNOWLEDGEMENTS

Thanks and appreciation to some very special people. My mother, Jo Ann Cornwell Rupp, photographic assistance; my father, Richard Rupp, assistance; A. Glenn Mandeville, for his friendship and advice; Barbara Miller, a good friend; and to all my other good friends and relatives. Also my doll club, Derby City Doll Club of Kentucky for sponsoring my "Welcome To BARBIE®town U.S.A." exhibit at our 1988 UFDC Region 8 Conference, Vive Les Bebes.

FRONT COVER: *Left to Right:* The **BARBIE®** *Le Nouveau theatre De La Mode* (1985) was especially created by Billy Boy for Mattel France to commemorate 26 years of BARBIE® doll. This was a 10,000 limited edition. The one shown is signed by Billy Boy and the majority were not! The booklets are from Mattel France in collaboration with Billy Boy for his train exposition and from the United States "BARBIE® On Tour". The brunette doll is *Feelin' Groovy BARBIE® Doll* (1986) – All are rare and hard to find. Evans Furs designed for distribution in Lazarus Department Stores a BARBIE® doll size mink coat. It came in a Lara's Fur Accessories box with the BARBIE® doll, and the suggested retail price was $200.00. **BARBIE®'s Classy Corvette** (1976) was a Department Store Special. **BARBIE® Hundesede (dog sled)** c. 1981 was available in Scandinavian nations. Very, very, rare. This rare and hard to find **BARBIE® & Skipper® Travel Trunk** is a SPP trunk dated 1965. This is often referred to as "Picnic"' in reference to the very detailed graphic. It is one of the author's personal favorites.

BACK COVER: The **BARBIE®** *Dream House* was the BARBIE® doll's first house. Shown is the interior of the house. *Mattel, Inc. 1994 BARBIE® 35th Anniversary BARBIE® Festival*. Items from the limited edition sale collection are: *35th Anniversary Festival BARBIE®*, *Nostalgic 35th Anniversary Gift Set*, signed by Ruth Handler, and signed Ruth Handler and Elliot Handler 1962 photograph. Rare.

Additional copies of this book may be purchased at $19.95 (plus postage and handling) from

Hobby House Press, Inc.
1 Corporate Drive
Grantsville, Maryland 21536
1-800-554-1447
or from your favorite bookstore or dealer.

ISBN: 0-87588-450-4

TABLE OF CONTENTS

See Chapter 3 for more information.

See Chapter 12 for more information.

See Chapter 16 for more information.

INTRODUCTION

Mattel Toys, Inc. introduced the BARBIE® doll on March 9, 1959 at the New York Toy Fair. She was created as a three-dimensional fashion model whose concept was based on paper dolls. The individually sold fashions featured original titles which allow imaginative play. Children were soon writing letters to Mattel Toys, Inc. wanting to learn more about the "World of BARBIE® doll."

In response to children's inquiries, the world of BARBIE® doll was rapidly growing. BARBIE® doll was soon developing her own persona via accessories. She was solo in the spotlight until she met her campus hero boyfriend, Ken® doll who was introduced in 1961 and little sister, Skipper® doll was introduced in 1964. Through the years BARBIE® doll has been supported by friends, family, and pets. Friends, Midge® doll, Allen® doll, P.J.™ doll, Stacey® doll, Steffie® doll, cousin Francie® doll, tiny twin sister, Tutti® doll, tiny twin brother, Todd® doll, Fluff™ Kitten, Dallas™ Golden Palomino, Prince™ French Poodle, and etc. have played supporting roles in BARBIE® doll adventures.

In essence BARBIE® doll, family, friends, and pets have become characters in an unfolding story in twentieth century culture. The images they portrayed have depicted auspicious historical, and various unforgettable moments throughout the past 36 years. BARBIE® doll, family, and friends have participated in the 1974 Olympics, and the Ice Capades 50th Anniversary to name a couple of events.

The extraordinary accessories began in 1961 and all accessories to date are significant in the background of BARBIE® doll, family, friends, and pet characterization. The accessories are an important element to the "World of BARBIE® doll". BARBIE® doll has resided in a "Dream House", "Surprise House" and other homes. She has had constant mobilization traveling the open road in her automobile collection which began with an Austin Healy sports car or whether riding her "10 Speeder". BARBIE® doll and Ken® doll have flown the friendly skies for United Airlines abroad the"Friend Ship". The "Dream Carriage" ride under the stars has made for an enchanted evening. Fashionable BARBIE® doll has always dressed to nines in casual and haute couture. She is a suburban shopper like innumerable women, including myself, will go to the "Fashion Shop", "Fashion Plaza" or "Dream Store", looking for something new to wear because (even though the rod in the closet has fallen down from being too full) there is nothing to wear! BARBIE® doll has been able to maintain her ideal weight of 110 pounds, while having "Fun at McDonald®'s" and enjoying "Little Debbie Snack Cakes".

Fun and enjoyment are your number one priority when collecting BARBIE® dolls and accessories. Remember, collect what you enjoy and enjoy what you collect.

The format of this book has many lists to assist you, the collector, in your quest to find the *Treasury of BARBIE® Doll Accessories.*

COLLECTING ACCESSORIES

I am a first generation to play-act with BARBIE® doll, Ken® doll, Skipper® doll, their family, friends, and accessories. All facets involving the world of BARBIE® doll were part of my childhood. Some of you may have heard of "Welcome To BARBIE®town U.S.A." which is my collection that was exhibited as "Welcome to BARBIE®town U.S.A." in 1988 at UFDC convention. When looking through the illustrations in this book you can see the ways in which I display the "Welcome to BARBIE®town U.S.A." dolls and accessories in my collection and exhibits.

One very significant element in the longevity of the BARBIE® doll world is the enthusiasts. The first "BARBIE® Fan Club" reached one million members in 1965. Collectors have been annually attending "The National BARBIE® doll Convention" since 1980.

There are many types of BARBIE® doll collectors: those of us who collect "everything" BARBIE® doll, others who collect dolls and fashions, and some individuals who collect only BARBIE® dolls. "Everything" BARBIE® doll collector's viewpoint is to have a retrospective with the characters and accessories representing a time-capsule in the days of our lives.

A very important factor is to have the correct era dolls in their appropriate fashion and to display the accessories with the correct era dolls. One who collect the dolls and fashions will have a representation of twentieth century fashions.

As BARBIE® doll collectors, we must not forget BARBIE® doll's original concept. She was created as a fashion doll and the accessories were toys. Those who collect only the dolls are missing out on the "true" world of BARBIE® doll. Accessories have made BARBIE® doll the phenomenal that she is today.

In the realm of BARBIE® doll collecting, there is something for everyone to have a speciality interest. Many collectors cross over into other speciality interests. Such as toy, paper doll, children's storybooks, McDonald®'s, games, calendars, greeting cards, ornaments, tea sets, view-master reels, and various other collections. In today's world there is a collector for everything. Items of today and yesterday are tomorrow's yesteryears nostalgia. Take pleasure in your collection by collecting the accessories you enjoy.

Chapter 1

PAPER DOLL HISTORY AND CHRONOLOGY

The BARBIE™ doll debut was in 1959. Fourteen years earlier in 1945, Mattel's co-founder Ruth Handler saw her four year old daughter playing with paper dolls of adult figures and fashions. This inspired her to create a three-dimensional doll with wardrobe named BARBIE™ doll after her daughter Barbara.

BARBIE™ paper dolls became available in 1962, three years after the debut of BARBIE™ doll. The Western Publishing Co., Inc. began production, under license from Mattel, Inc., on a line of paper dolls based on the BARBIE™ doll and fashions.

There have been several paper doll artists through the years. Al Anderson designed the paper dolls of the 1960's and early 1970's. Barb Rausch has designed some paper dolls but is best known as an illustrator. The well-known paper doll artist, Tom Tierney has drawn paper dolls of both BARBIE™ doll and other famous people.

Western Publishing Co., Inc. has printed paper dolls under three names: Whitman, Golden, and Golden Books. Whitman was seen on the BARBIE™ paper dolls from 1962 until 1984. Golden was first seen in 1980 and continued to be used through 1994. Both Whitman and Golden have produced paper doll books and boxed paper doll sets. Golden Books was first seen on 1994 paper doll books.

In 1989, the Peck-Gandré Collection produced under license from Mattel, Inc., *Nostalgic BARBIE™* and *Nostalgic Ken™*. The Peck Aubry Collection began a new nostalgic BARBIE™ doll collection of paper dolls in 1994.

Western Publishing Co., Inc. continues to produce BARBIE™, family and friends paper dolls, three decades after the first five-color BARBIE™ paper doll rolled off the press. In 1990, Western Publishing Co., Inc. proclaimed themselves as the largest commercial paper doll manufacturer.

The following BARBIE™, family, and friends paper dolls were available through the years since 1962. They are listed chronologically by copyright date.

1 *Skipper® , BARBIE®'s Little Sister* c. 1962, a Whitman Paper Doll Book.

2. The first Whitman paper doll book to feature BARBIE® and Ken® doll, entitled ***BARBIE® and Ken™*** *c. 1962* was drawn by Al Anderson.

3

4

1962
Whitman Paper Doll Books
  BARBIE™ #1962
  Skipper®, Barbie®'s Little Sister #1962
  BARBIE® and Ken™ #1963 BK, #1971:59
  BARBIE® Doll Cut-Outs #1963

Whitman Boxed Paper Doll Sets
  BARBIE™ #4601
  BARBIE™ *and Ken*™ *Suitcase/Traveling Dolls* #4797

1963
Whitman Paper Doll Books
  BARBIE™ #11001, #4601
  BARBIE™ *and Ken*™ #1976 BK 63
  BARBIE™, *Ken*™ *and Midge®* #1976 BKM 63
  Midge®, BARBIE™*'s Best Friend Cut-Outs* #1962-29

Whitman Boxed Paper Doll Sets
  BARBIE™ *and Ken*™ #4797 BK63, #4797-100

1964
Whitman Paper Doll Books
  BARBIE™ *and Skipper®* #1944
  BARBIE™ *Costume Dolls* #1979-59

Whitman Boxed Paper Doll Sets
  BARBIE™ *Fashion Window Wardrobe* #4605 B65
  BARBIE™®, *Midge®, and Skipper®* #4793
  BARBIE™*'s Travel Wardrobe* #4616
  BARBIE™*'s Wedding Dress 'n Fashion Clothes*
      #4605 WD64
    Skipper®'s Day-by-Day Wardrobe #4607
    Skipper® & Skooter™*'s Four (4) Season Wardrobe*
      #4778

1965
Whitman Paper Doll Books
  Skipper®, BARBIE™*'s Little Sister* #1984
  Skooter™, *Skipper®'s Best Friend* #1985

Whitman Boxed Paper Doll Sets
  Skipper® Fashion Calendar Wardrobe #4607
  Skooter® Fashion Go-Round #4639
  BARBIE® and Midge® Travel Wardrobe #4785
  BARBIE®, Midge®, Skipper® #4793

1966
Whitman Paper Doll Books
  BARBIE®, Skipper®, Skooter™ #1976 BSS66
  Meet Francie®, BARBIE™*'s Modern Cousin &*
  Casey #1980

Whitman Boxed Paper Doll Sets
  BARBIE™ and Francie®, BARBIE™'s
Modern Cousin #4793 BF66

1967
Whitman Paper Doll Books
  BARBIE® has a new look! #1976, #1996
  Francie® #1094
  Francie®, BARBIE™*'s Modern Cousin & Casey,*
    Francie®'s Fun Friend #1986, 1989

3. ***BARBIE® has a new look!*** c. 1967, a Whitman
Paper Doll Book.
4. ***New 'N' Groovy P.J.***™ c. 1970, a Whitman Paper
Doll Book. On the right is a P.J.® paper doll
wearing one of her paper doll fashions.

Whitman Boxed Paper Doll Sets
BARBIE™ #4785 B67
Tutti #4622

1968 _____
Whitman Paper Doll Books
BARBIE™, *Christie and Stacey*™ *BARBIE*™'s
New Friends #1976-59/68
Tutti, BARBIE™ *& Skipper*®'s *Tiny Sister* #1991

1969 _____
Whitman Paper Doll Books
BARBIE™ *Dolls and Clothes* #1976 B69

Whitman Boxed Paper Doll Sets
BARBIE™, *2 Magic Dolls with Stay on Clothes* #4763

1970 _____
Whitman Paper Doll Books
BARBIE™ *and Ken*™ #1976 BK70
New 'N' Groovy P.J.® #1981

1971 _____
Whitman Paper Doll Books
Groovy World of BARBIE™ *& Her Friends* #1976 B71
P.J.® *Cover Girl* #1981 PJ71
World of BARBIE™ #1987 PJ71

Whitman Boxed Paper Doll Sets
BARBIE™ #4735
BARBIE™ *Magic* #4331
New "N' Groovy P.J.® #4332

1972 _____
Whitman Paper Doll Books
Paper Doll Fashions/P.J.® *and*
BARBIE™ #1975
Paper Doll Fashions Groovy P.J.®
#1974
Pos'n' BARBIE™ #1875
Malibu BARBIE™/*The Sun Set* #1994

Whitman Boxed Paper Doll Sets
Malibu BARBIE™ #1996
Malibu P.J.® #4718
World of BARBIE™ #4376-B
World of BARBIE™ *Play Fun*
Box #4343

1973 _____
Whitman Paper Doll Books
BARBIE™ *& P.J.*®/*A Camping*
Adventure #1971 73
BARBIE™'s *Boutique*® #1947-1
BARBIE™ *Country Camper* #1990-69
BARBIE®'s *Friend Ship* #1996-79
Francie® *with Grow 'N Pretty Hair* #1982-79
Paper Doll Fashions/Hi, I'm Skipper® #1969
Malibu Francie® #1955
Malibu Skipper® #1945-2
Quick Curl BARBIE™ *and Her Friends* #1984-79

Whitman Boxed Paper Doll Sets
BARBIE™'s *Magic Paper Dolls* #4322
BARBIE™ *Country Camper and Paper Doll* #4347

5

6

5. *BARBIE*™'s *Boutique*® c. 1973, a Whitman Paper
Doll Book.
6. *Malibu Francie*™ and *Malibu Skipper*® both c. 1973,
Whitman Paper Doll Books.

7

8

9

7. *Fashion Photo® BARBIE® and P.J.®*
   c. 1978, a Whitman Paper Doll Book.
8. *BARBIE®'s Friend Ship* c. 1973, a Whitman
   Paper Doll Book.
9. *BARBIE®'s Design-A-Fashion Paper Doll Kit*
   was a 1979 Whitman Boxed Paper Doll Set.
   The kit contains materials to design paper
   doll fashions (six mix 'n' match patterns,
   tracing tissue, and colored pencils). This set
   is unique with its concept and 13in (33cm)
   BARBIE® paper doll.

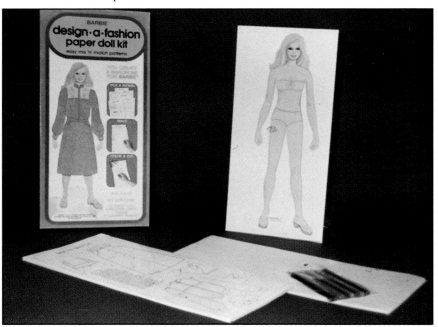

1979 _____

Whitman Boxed Paper Doll Sets
BARBIE®'s Design-A-Fashion Paper Doll Kit #4328-20
Skipper®'s Design-A-Fashion Paper Doll Kit #4329-21

1980 _____

Whitman Paper Doll Books
BARBIE® and Skipper®/Campsite at Lucky Lake #1836-31
Super Teen Skipper® #1982-33

Golden Paper Doll Books
BARBIE® and Skipper®/Campsite at Lucky Lake #1836-41

Whitman Boxed Paper Doll Sets
Pretty Changes BARBIE™ #7410

1981 _____

Whitman Paper Doll Books
BARBIE® #7408
Pretty Changes BARBIE™ #1982-34

Golden Paper Doll Books
Pretty Changes BARBIE® #1982-42

Whitman Boxed Paper Doll Sets
BARBIE™ #74088-21
BARBIE™ and Her 27-Piece Wardrobe #7408-B-1
Super Teen Skipper® & Scott #7408-C-1

1982 _____

Whitman Paper Doll Books
Golden Dream BARBIE™ #1983-43
Western BARBIE™ #1982-43

Golden Paper Doll Books
Western BARBIE™ #1982-43 G

Whitman Boxed Paper Doll Sets
Golden Dream BARBIE™ #7408C
Malibu BARBIE™ #7408-E
Western BARBIE™ #7408-H
BARBIE™ Design-A-Fashion Paper Doll Kit #4328-21
Skipper® Design-A-Fashion Paper Doll Kit #4329-21

1983 _____

Whitman Paper Doll Books
BARBIE™ & Skipper® #1944

Golden Paper Doll Books
Angel Face BARBIE™ #1982-45
Paper Doll Playbook/Pink & Pretty BARBIE™ #1838-45
Pink & Pretty BARBIE™ #1983-44
Sunsational Malibu BARBIE™ #1982-44
Twirly Curls BARBIE™ #1982-46

Golden Boxed Paper Doll Sets
(Angel Face) BARBIE™ Paper Doll #7407-E
Pink & Pretty BARBIE™ #7411-B
Western Skipper® #7411-C

1984 _____

Whitman Paper Doll Books
BARBIE™ and Ken™ #1985-51 M

10

11

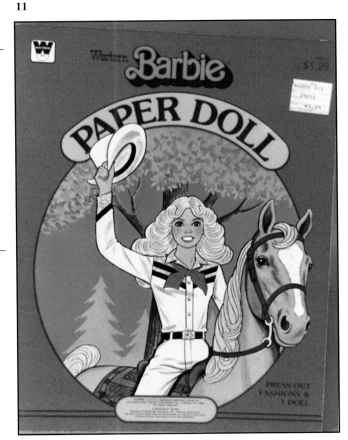

10. *BARBIE® and Skipper®/Campsite at Lucky Lake* c. 1980, a Golden Paper Doll Book.

11. *Western BARBIE™* a 1982 Whitman Paper Doll Book.

12

13

Golden Paper Doll Books
BARBIE™ & Ken #1527
BARBIE™ Christmas Time
#1731-129
BARBIE™ "FANTASY" #1982-47
Crystal BARBIE™ #1983-46

Golden Boxed Paper Doll Sets
Crystal BARBIE™ #7407-B

1985 _____

Golden Paper Doll Books
Day-to-Night BARBIE® #1982-48
Great Shape BARBIE™ #1982-49
Peaches 'n Cream BARBIE™
#1983-48

1986 _____

Golden Paper Doll Books
BARBIE® and the ROCKERS™ #1528
Tropical BARBIE® #1523

1987 _____

Golden Paper Doll Books
Jewel Secrets BARBIE® #1537

1988 _____

Golden Paper Doll Books
Perfume Pretty BARBIE™ #1500

1989 _____

Golden Paper Doll Books
SuperStar BARBIE® #1537-2

Peck-Gandré™ Presents
Nostalgic Blonde BARBIE™
Nostalgic Brunette BARBIE™
Nostalgic Ken™

1990 _____

Golden Paper Doll Books
BARBIE™ #1502-3

14

12. *Pink & Pretty BARBIE™* and *Paper Doll Playbook/Pink & Pretty BARBIE™* both 1983 Golden Paper Doll Books.
13. *(Angel Face) BARBIE™ Paper Doll* a 1983 Golden Boxed Paper Doll Set and *Crystal™ BARBIE™* a 1984 Golden Boxed Paper Doll Set.
14. *BARBIE® & Ken®* c. 1984, a Golden Paper Doll Book.

(Paris Pretty Fashion) BARBIE™ #1532-2
(Western Fun) BARBIE™ #1502
BARBIE™ #1502-1

Golden Deluxe Paper Doll (More Fashions) Books
Deluxe Paper Doll BARBIE® #1699
Deluxe Paper Doll BARBIE® #1690
Deluxe Paper Doll BARBIE® #1690-2

1991
Golden Paper Doll Books
(SuperStar) BARBIE™ #1537-3
BARBIE™ #1502-2

Golden Deluxe Paper Doll (More Fashions) Books
Deluxe Paper Doll BARBIE™ #1690-1
Deluxe Paper Doll BARBIE™ #1695
Deluxe Paper Doll BARBIE™ #1695-1
Deluxe Paper Doll BARBIE™ #1690-2

Golden Boxed Paper Doll Sets
BARBIE™ #5552

Price Stern Sloan
BARBIE™ *and the Beat*™ *on Tour/*
Play Set with 3-D Movable Dolls

1992
Golden Paper Doll Books
BARBIE™ #1502-3
BARBIE™ #1690-2

1993
Golden Paper Doll Books
BARBIE™ #1502-4
BARBIE™ #1502-5

Golden Boxed Paper Doll Sets
BARBIE™ *Paper Doll* #5559
BARBIE™ *Paper Doll* #5570

15

16

17

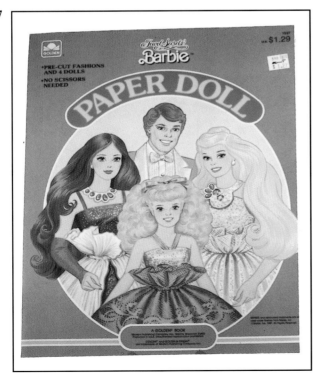

15. **Day-to-Night BARBIE**® c. 1985, a Golden Paper Doll Book created by Tom Tierney.
16. **BARBIE® and The Rockers**™ c. 1986, a Golden Paper Doll Book.
17. **Jewel Secrets BARBIE**® c. 1987, a Golden Paper Doll Book.

18

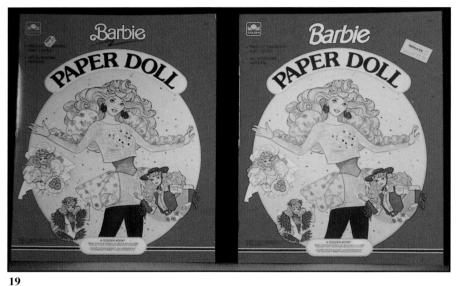

19

20

21

22

1994

Golden Deluxe Edition Paper Doll Books
BARBIE™ #2371
BARBIE™ #2381

Golden Books Deluxe Edition Paper Doll Books
BARBIE™ #2018

The Peck Aubry Collection
The 1959 (Number One) BARBIE®
The 1961 (Bubble Cut) BARBIE®
The 1964 (Ponytail Swirl) BARBIE®

1995

The Peck Aubry Collection
The 1965 (American Girl) BARBIE™

18. Two *SuperStar BARBIE*® Golden Paper Doll Books. Book on the left is c. 1989 and book on the right is c. 1991, 1989. They have the exact same contents; their covers are different. The copyright 1989 cover is illustrated and the copyright 1991, 1989 edition has a photo art cover.

19. *BARBIE*® *Paper Doll Books* c. 1990, Golden Paper doll books using the two logos. In the middle of the year Mattel, Inc. changed the BARBIE™ logo.

20. This 5-1/2in (14cm) by 4in (10cm) *BARBIE*® *Paper Doll Cut-Outs* c. 1993, a Golden Paper Doll Book.

21. *BARBIE*® *and The Beat*™ *On Tour/Playset* with 3-D Movable Paper Dolls c.1991, by Price Stern Sloan.

22. *BARBIE*® *Doll Cut-Outs* c. 1962 featured the Bubble Cut BARBIE® doll. This Whitman Paper Doll Book was drawn by Al Anderson.

23

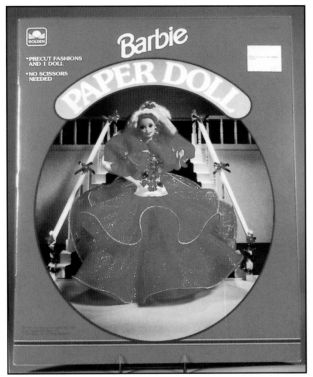

25

24

26

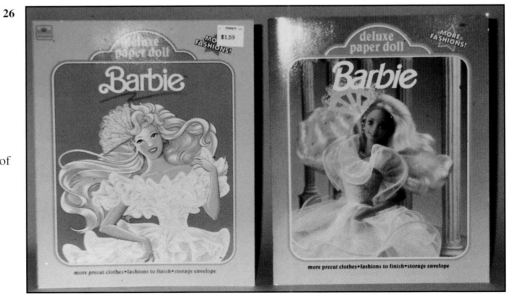

23. Peck-Gandré™ Presents (available in 1989) *Nostalgic Blonde BARBIE*™, *Nostalgic Ken*™, and *Nostalgic Brunette BARBIE*™. The paper doll fashions in these sets authentically depict the early fashions.

24. *BARBIE*® c. 1993, a Golden Paper Doll Book. Photo art cover of the 1993, *Happy Holidays BARBIE*® *doll*.

25. *BARBIE*® c. 1994, a Golden Deluxe Edition Paper Doll.

26. The *BARBIE*® *Golden Deluxe Paper Doll* (More Fashions) books of 1990 and 1991.

27

28

29

30

31

27. *1959 (Number One) BARBIE , 1961 (Bubble Cut) BARBIE ",* and *1964 (Ponytail Swirl) BARBIE* paper dolls were available in 1994 by the Peck Aubry Collection.

28. *BARBIE Deluxe Paper Doll* c. 1992, a Golden Paper Doll Book.

29. *BARBIE   Paper Doll* boxed sets made under license by Golden c. 1993. The set on the left is #5559 and on the right is #5570. Both are hard to find.

30. *BARBIE Skipper , Skooter* c. 1966, a Whitman Paper Doll Book.

31. *BARBIE* c. 1991, a Golden Boxed Paper Doll Set.

Chapter 2

TRAVELING WITH BARBIE® DOLL

The 1961 Mattel, Inc., catalogue stated that they had licensed a BARBIE® Doll Case designed exclusively for BARBIE® doll and her wardrobe. Orders would be accepted by Standard Plastics, Inc. of South Plainfield, New Jersey.

It is this author's opinion that Standard Plastics, Inc., designated the "Ponytail©" logo on early cases and various vinyl items to depict and illustrate BARBIE® doll with her ponytail hair style.

Standard Plastics, Inc. is most often referred to as Standard Plastic Products, Inc., (SPP). The SPP logo was on their wares beginning circa 1961 through circa 1965. Standard Plastic Productions, Inc. made doll cases, carry-alls, wallets, change purses, pencil cases, notebook ring binders, deskettes, dictionaries, photo portfolios, and snip 'n scraps books.

Mattel, Inc. acquired Standard Plastic Products (SPP) as a subsidiary in 1965.

Throughout the years there has been a variety of cases and trunks. The fundamental particularity distinguishing cases and trunks is the number of dolls they will hold. Cases will carry at least one doll or two dolls maximum. Trunks will hold two, three, and four dolls. Both have hanging bars for hanging up doll apparel. Cases and trunks have been either produced for BARBIE® doll, family, and friends individually or conjointly.

Additionally there have been travel totes, luggage, and book bags produced in child-size and BARBIE® doll size. These items in conjunction with cases and trunks have been illustrated with BARBIE® doll, family, friends and fashions in assorted themes.

Mattel, Inc. has continued to produce and given permission under license to various companies for case and other item manufacturing. Some items have been store exclusives; while others were distributed far and near.

32. BARBIE® doll's British Chum, Stacey™ doll is wearing "London Tour". The four-piece *luggage set* (inside the cosmetic bag is a removable tray) came in robin-egg-blue, cream beige, and turquoise. It was an unlicensed (1965 to 1971) product, although it can be seen in BARBIE®'s Around The World Trip View-Master Reels.

33

34

35

36

37

33. A Titian bubblecut BARBIE® doll is wearing *Rain Coat* fashion and BARBIE® doll friend, Midge® doll is wearing *Sorority Meeting*. The ***SPP BARBIE® and Midge® case*** is 1964.

34. This rare and hard to find ***BARBIE® & Skipper® Travel Trunk*** is a SPP trunk dated 1965. This is often referred to as "Picnic" in reference to the very detailed graphic. It is one of the author's personal favorites.

35. A Titian ponytail BARBIE® doll is wearing *Winter Holiday* fashion and beside her is an early *Ponytail c.* case without the BARBIE™ logo.

36. *Skipper® doll case* is a SPP dated 1964.

37. ***BARBIE®, Francie®, and Skipper® Doll Trunk*** is dated 1965 and was made by Mattel, Inc. This trunk is hard to find.

38

39

40

41

42

38. A magazine ad from 1966 showing *Tutti's Play House*.

39. *The World of BARBIE® doll case* c. 1968 and *The World of BARBIE® doll trunk* c. 1968 were both made by Mattel, Inc.

40. *BARBIE® Mountain Ski Cabin doll case* c. 1972 made by Mattel, Inc. as a Sears® exclusive in 1972 and 1974 (it was not available in 1973). This case is hard to find.

41. The very cute and hard to find *Skipper® & Skooter® Case* is dated 1965, Mattel, Inc. This case is shown with Skipper® doll, Skooter® doll and a sandcastle (a souvenir from Florida).

42. There have been various hanger packages made through the years. The small hangers do hold BARBIE® doll garments; although it is not recommended for preserving fashions.

43

44

45

43. The **BARBIE®** *Mountain Ski Cabin doll case* (1972) interior. Although, BARBIE® doll in *Ski Queen* (a 1963 fashion) and Ken® doll in *Ski Champion* (a 1963 fashion) are of a different era from the case – they look suited for it.

44. The **BARBIE®** *and Steffie® Sleep 'N Keep Case* (1972) interior.

45. The last Sears® exclusive **BARBIE®** *Sleep 'N Keep Case* is dated 1977 and was available to 1979. The BARBIE® dolls are wearing the same nightgowns as those seen in the graphic. These nightgowns were *BARBIE® Get-Ups 'N Go #9743* (1977) and *BARBIE® Best Buy #9157* (1976).

OPPOSITE PAGE:

46. Pencil cases made under license by ADI in 1983.

47. **BARBIE®** *and Steffie® Sleep 'N Keep Case* is dated 1969 Mattel, Inc. but was not released until 1972. This hard to find case was a Sears® exclusive. The dolls are Walk Lively BARBIE® doll and friend, Walk Lively Steffie® doll.

48. The **BARBIE®** *Sleep 'N Keep Case* interior.

49. **BARBIE®** *Style book bag and carry-all* was made by Mattel, Inc. in 1990. Also shown is an ad promoting these and various other products.

50. Two expand-a-files were under license to Applause, Inc. in 1990.

46

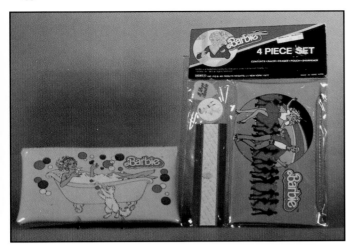

47

48

49

50

51

52

53

51. *BARBIE® On Madison* is a FAO Schwarz exclusive BARBIE® doll boutique of merchandise available in 1992. Shown is the **BARBIE® On Madison Case, BARBIE® On Madison Doll,** and **BARBIE® On Madison Watch.**
52. **BARBIE® Tons of Drawers** was a 1993 carry case made under license by Tara Toy Corp.
53. **BARBIE® Hollywood Suitcase** available in 1993, made under license by Ero Industries, Inc. The doll is **Hollywood Hair Chevelure BARBIE® doll**, an European Edition.

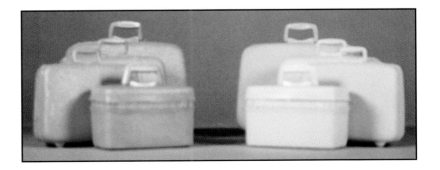

54. The interior of **Tutti® Playhouse** has a bed with her name on the head board, a closet (without a door), and table with two chairs (all of which are attached).
55. The "**BARBIE™ Take-A-Long**" c. 1995 was produced under license by Tara Toy Corp. This trunk is a pullman and holds six dolls.
56. **Tutti® Playhouse** 1966 was made by Mattel, Inc.'s subsidiary SSP. This case came with Tutti® doll, BARBIE® doll, and Skipper® doll's tiny little sister. It is hard to find the case and rare when **Tutti®** doll is with it.
57. **BARBIE® Doll Scale Luggage** was available 1965 to 1971 can be opened and packed.

Chapter 3

FAN CLUBS AND PERIODICALS

The *BARBIE® Fan Club* began in 1962. *Mattel Barbie Magazine* premiered as a response and correspondence to the mail Mattel, Inc. had received. The subscription cost was $1.00 for six issues, wallet-size *BARBIE® Fan Club* identification card, and a BARBIE® doll emblem to sew on apparel.

Dell Publishing Company, Inc. was authorized by Mattel, Inc. in 1962 to do periodical comic magazines. The comic magazine stories had plots revolving around the *BARBIE® Fan Club*. Each of the following five issues were called *BARBIE® and Ken*™:

May - July 1962, Number 01-053-207
August - October 1962, Number 12-053-210
May - July 1963, Number 12-053-307
August - October 1963, Number 12-053-310
November - January 1964, Number 12-053-401

Mattel, Inc. received an estimated 20,000 letters per week addressed to BARBIE® doll. The *BARBIE® Fan Club* had a half-million members world-wide in 1964. Membership was free. Application forms were found in fashion booklets and the club was promoted in television commercials. Those who enrolled in the (United States of America) National BARBIE® Fan Club received in their membership kit – a letter from BARBIE® doll, membership card, and BARBIE® doll Fan Club badge. The National Fan Club had 8,500 chapters. *BARBIE® Magazine,* a bi-monthly publication about the world of BARBIE® doll, family and friends, was the official publication of the *BARBIE® Fan Club.*

The club held a contest to reach one million members by September 15, 1965. The grand-prize was a trip for two to the winner's choice destination of either Disneyland® or the New York World's Fair.

National BARBIE® Fan Club membership reached 1,500,000 in 1968. The International BARBIE® Club had 250,000 members. Mattel, Inc. was selling in over sixty countries including: West Germany, Italy, France, Spain, England, Australia, Bahamas, Israel, Japan, Canada, and Mexico.

The 1969 fashion booklets had an insert form to

58

58. Dell *BARBIE® and Ken*™ *comic magazines* are from left to right: *Top row:* May-July 1962, August-October 1962. *Bottom row:* May-July 1963, August-October 1963, and November-January 1965. Each is very rare and hard to find.

join the New BARBIE® Fan Club for $2.00. Sears® offered the exact membership kit in 1970 for $1.00. This membership kit included BARBIE® doll fashion "Salute To Silver", portrait (of BARBIE® doll, family, and friends), membership certificate, membership card, and an issue of *BARBIE® Talk* magazine. In 1970 and 1971 fashion booklets, the membership kit offer changed. Members would receive a BARBIE® doll child-size charm bracelet instead of the fashion. Every other aspect remained the same. These fan clubs were ceased circa 1972.

A revived *BARBIE® Fan Club* was advertised in selected consumer magazines in May 1981. Club applications were found in various doll boxes and accessory boxes. The membership fee was $5.00. Each member received in their membership kit a welcome letter, autographed picture of BARBIE® doll, official membership card, iron-on "I'm a BARBIE® Fan" patch, a poster to color, and a sun visor. The members also received quarterly issues of *BARBIE® Fan Club News*. The BARBIE® Fan Club underwent a change in 1984 with a new *BARBIE® – The Magazine for Girls*.

Marvel Entertainment, under license from Mattel, Inc., began two comic book series, "BARBIE®" and "BARBIE® Fashion" in 1990.

BARBIE® doll's 35th anniversary of worldwide sales in 140 nations was celebrated in 1995. Two dolls are sold every second somewhere in the world.

59

60

61

59. The rarest *BARBIE® and Ken™ Dell comic magazine* issue is the November-January 1965 issue. The cover shows BARBIE® doll wearing the formal *Sophisticated Lady* and Ken® in *Tuxedo*.
60. The *New BARBIE® Fan Club* 1969, membership kit.
61. The *New BARBIE® Fan Club* official magazine was *BARBIE® Talk* named after the technology of *Talking BARBIE® doll* seen here with friends, *Talking Stacey™ doll* and *Talking P.J.™ doll*.

62

63

64

65

66

62. A revived **BARBIE**® **Fan Club** was advertised in selected consumer magazines in 1981. The booklet, *BARBIE*® *Doll Through The Years* was available free from Mattel, Inc. from 1977 to 1983.

63. The 1989 Target® exclusive, **BARBIE**® **The Magazine for Girls 30th Anniversary** issue came with a fashion.

64. The *Happy Holiday BARBIE*™ *doll* series began in 1988 and **BARBIE**® **The Magazine for Girls** has put each year's *Happy Holiday BARBIE*™ *doll* on the cover.

65. **BARBIE**® – **The Magazine For Girls** has been available since 1984.

66. Marvel Entertainment began in 1990 two comic book series, **BARBIE**® and **BARBIE**® **Fashion**.

Chapter 4

BARBIE® DOLL STORY BOOKS

The children's storybooks contributed to BARBIE® doll's delineation stages of characterizations. BARBIE® doll, family, and friends have continued to project their images in their unfolding stories.

Random House Books under license from Mattel, Inc. began production in 1962 of a hardcover BARBIE® doll storybook series. The books had good moral stories. BARBIE® doll was given a middle name and a surname; Barbie Millicent Roberts. Ken® doll was given a surname as well; Ken Carson. Their last names were derived from the Mattel, Inc. advertising agency at the time, Carson/Roberts.

The authors and illustrators of the fourteen book series were Cynthia Lawrence, Bette Lou Maybee, Eleanor Woolin, Marianne Duest, Robert Patterson, and Carl Memling. Some books are numbered on the spine in a small BARBIE® doll head silhouette; on the dust jacket and the book itself. The books and copyright dates are listed as follows:

The World of BARBIE® c. 1962
#1 *Here's BARBIE®* c. 1962
#2 *BARBIE®'s Fashion Success* c. 1962
#3 *BARBIE®'s New York Summer* c. 1962
#4 *BARBIE® and Ken®* c. 1963
#5 *BARBIE® Solves a Mystery* c. 1963
#6 *BARBIE® Hawaiian Holiday* c. 1963
#7 *BARBIE® Secret* c. 1964
#8 *BARBIE® In Television* c. 1964
#9 *BARBIE®, Midge® and Ken®* c. 1964
BARBIE® Easy As Pie Cookbook c. 1964
#10 *BARBIE®'s Candy Striped Summer* c. 1965
#11 *BARBIE® and Ghost Town Mystery* c. 1965
Happy-Go-Lucky Skipper® c. 1965

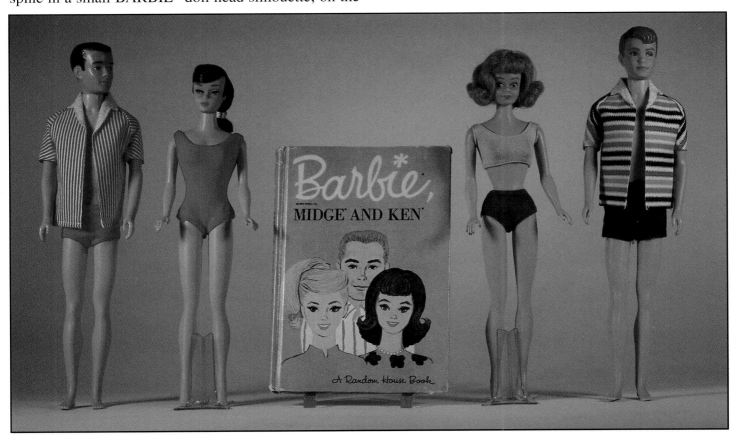

67

67. Random House Books began a BARBIE® doll storybook series. The book shown here is *#9 BARBIE®, Midge® and Ken®* c. 1964.

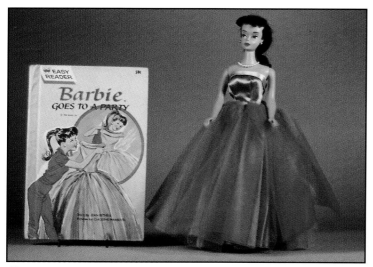

68

Wonder Books under license from Mattel, Inc. published four storybooks in 1964. These storybooks were written and drawn by Jean Bethell, Ellen Lenhart, and Claudine Nankivel. The following titles were available:

BARBIE® The Baby Sitter...hardcover book
BARBIE® Goes To A Party...hardcover book
BARBIE®'s Adventures - "To Read Aloud"...paperback
Portrait of Skipper® (The Story Book of Skipper® - A New Doll)...paperback book

Western Publishing Company, Inc. has published an assortment of children's storybooks throughout the years. They have published under "A Tell-A-Tale® Book(s)", "A Little Golden Book®", "Whitman®", "Golden®" and "Golden Sound Story". All have been published under license from Mattel, Inc. The following Western Publishing Company, Inc. storybooks are listed under registered trademark:

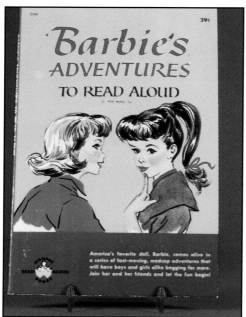

69

70

71

68. ***BARBIE® Goes To A Party*** c. 1964, published by Wonder Books.
69. ***BARBIE®'s Adventures – "To Read Aloud"*** c. 1964, published by Wonder Books.
70. ***Portrait of Skipper®, The Story Book of Skipper® A New Doll*** c. 1964, published by Wonder Books.
71. ***BARBIE® and Skipper® Go Camping*** c. 1977, 1973, a Whitman® – "A Tell-A-Tale®" storybook.

Whitman® – A Tell-A-Tale®

BARBIE and Skipper Go Camping by Eileen Daly. This storybook was first copyrighted in 1973 and renewed in 1977 with a cover change.

Golden® – A Tell-A-Tale®

BARBIE On Skates c. 1992, written by Rita Balducci and illustrated by Tom Tierney.

Golden®

My Very Own Diary By BARBIE – You Help BARBIE Write Her Diary c. 1985, written by Laura Westlake

BARBIE and The Rockers The Hottest Group In Town c. 1987, written by Deborah Kovacs and illustrated by Tom Tierney

BARBIE and The Rockers The Fan c. 1987, written by Teddy Slater and illustrated by Tom Tierney

BARBIE A Picnic Surprise book and tape c. 1990, written by Leslie McGuire and illustrated by Art Ellis and Kim Ellis

BARBIE The Big Splash book and tape c. 1992, written by Barbara Slate and illustrated by Tom Tierney

BARBIE Show Time! c. 1992, written by Patricia Jensen

A Little Golden Book line began in 1942. Since then there have been approximately 1,000 titles. The first BARBIE doll story was their 125th title. They are listed as follows:

BARBIE c. 1974, written and illustrated by Betty Biesterveld

The Fairy Princess SuperStar BARBIE c. 1977, written by Anne Foster and illustrated by Jim Robison and Fred Irwin

The Missing Wedding Dress Featuring BARBIE c. 1986, written by Karen Krugman and illustrated by Laura Westlake

72

73.

72. BARBIE doll book marks have been made in a variety of designs by Antioch Publishing Company.
73. The complete set of **BARBIE doll – A Little Golden Book** storybooks is hard to find.

74

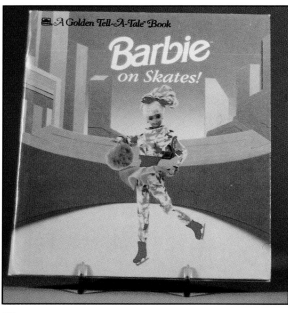

75

76

BARBIE® A Picnic Surprise c.1990, written by Leslie McGuire and illustrated by Art Ellis and Kim Ellis

BARBIE® The Big Splash c. 1992 and second edition c. 1993, written by Barbara Slate and illustrated by Tom Tierney

Very Busy BARBIE® c. 1993, written by Barbara Slate and illustrated by Winslow Mortimer

BARBIE® Soccer Coach c. 1995, written by Barbara Slate

Golden Sound Story® is a patented electronic storybook that uniquely plays music and sounds. The books are as follows:

BARBIE® The Island Resort Adventure c. 1992

BARBIE® Birthday Surprise For Skipper c. 1992

In 1983, Kid Stuff® under license from Mattel, Inc. produced the following four storybooks:

BARBIE®'s Camping Adventure
BARBIE® In The City
BARBIE®'s Neighborhood
BARBIE®'s Christmas Party

Hasbro, Inc. made under license from Mattel, Inc.:
BARBIE® in Dream Vacation in 1984.

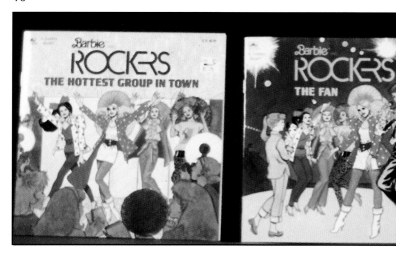

74. **My Very Own Diary by BARBIE®
– You Help BARBIE® Write Her
Diary** c. 1985 by Golden®.
75. **BARBIE® On Skates** c. 1992, a
Golden® – "A Tell-A-Tale".
76. Golden® published two storybooks
on **BARBIE® and The Rockers™**
illustrated by Tom Tierney.

Price-Stern-Sloan under license from Mattel, Inc. began a new series of books in 1993. The million printed book copies are distributed through book clubs and school book fairs. The following BARBIE® doll books have been printed:

#1   *The Mysterious Dude of Ghost Ranch*
#2   *Dancing The Night Away*
#3   *Wildlife Rescue*
#4   *Soda Shop Surprise*
#5   *The Phantom of Shrieking Pond*
#6   *Rollerblade Crusade*
#7   *Ballet Debut*
#8   *Holiday Magic*
#9   *Star-Swept Adventure*
#10   *Wild Horse Run*
#11   *Animal Escapades*
#12   *Mermaid Island*

The storybooks signify the history and juncture of BARBIE® doll, Ken® doll, and Skipper® doll, along with their family and friends.

77. **BARBIE® Show Time!** c. 1992, a Golden® storybook.
78. Golden® has done books and tapes of their various titles.

79

80

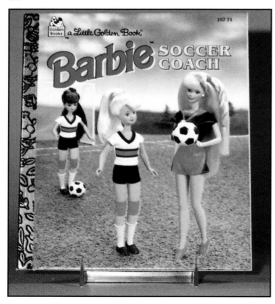

79. **_BARBIE® Birthday Surprise for Skipper®_** c. 1992 was second in the Golden Sound Story series.
80. **_BARBIE™ Soccer Coach_** c. 1995 is A Little Golden Book.
81. The patented electronic storybook, **_BARBIE® The Island Resort Adventure_** c. 1992 began a new Golden Sound Story series.

81

Chapter 5

BARBIE® DOLLHOUSES

BARBIE® doll, family and friends houses have come in assorted architectural designs, dimensions, and price ranges just like real-estate. Each house's interior design has represented its time period.

As follows is a list of the dollhouses:

1962 to 1965 ...*BARBIE®'s Dream House*
1964 to 1966 ...*BARBIE®'s New Dream House*
1965 ....*BARBIE® and Skipper®'s Deluxe
            Dream House (Sears® exclusive)*
1966 to 1967 ...*BARBIE® Family Deluxe House
            (Sears® exclusive)*
1966 ....*Francie™ House*
1966 ....*Skipper® Deluxe Dream House
            (Sears® exclusive)*
1967 to 1970 ...*BARBIE® Family House*
1967 ....*Francie™ and Casey™
            Studio House*
1968 ....*The World of BARBIE® House*
1969 to 1972 ...*World of BARBIE®
            Family House*
1970 to 1971 ...*BARBIE® Lively Livin' House*
1972 to 1974 ...*BARBIE® Surprise House*
1973 ....*BARBIE® Country Living Home*
1974 to 1979 ...*BARBIE® Townhouse*

The townhouse featured various graphics in it's original year of issue and again when it was reissued in 1984 and 1988 to 1989.

    1979 to 1987 ...*BARBIE® Dream House -
               Yellow*
    1988 to 1991 ...*BARBIE® Dream House -
               Pink*
    1983 to 1984 ...*BARBIE® Dream Cottage*
    1985 to 1989 ...*BARBIE® Glamour Home*

1990 to 1991 ...*The BARBIE® Magical Mansion*
1992 ....*BARBIE® Magic Sounds House*
1993 to 1994 ...*BARBIE® Fold 'N Fun House*
1994 ....*BARBIE®'s 3-in-1 House*
               FAO Schwarz exclusive

The following is a list of apartments:
1971 ....*Jamie™'s Penthouse*
               (Sears® exclusive)
1975 ....*BARBIE®'s Apartment*
               (Department Store Special)

82

82. The **BARBIE® Townhouse** was a top toy of the 1976 Christmas season.

83

84

85

The following is a listing of rooms:

1965 to 1966...*BARBIE®'s Kitchen and Dinette*
1965 to 1966...*Skipper®'s Dream Room*
1972 ....*Teen Dream Bedroom*
1972 ....*Livin' Room*
1972 ....*Cookin' Fun Kitchen*
1975 to 1976...*Country Kitchen*
1975 to 1976...*Studio Bedroom*
1975 to 1976...*Firelight Living Room*

BARBIE® doll has had nineteen homes, Ken® doll has had none and other family and friends have had five dwellings.

83. An advertisement for the ***BARBIE®
    Glamour Home***.
84. ***BARBIE® Kitchen and Dinette*** is shown
    with Titian Swirl Ponytail BARBIE® doll
    wearing *BARBIE®-Q Outfit*.
85. ***BARBIE® Dream House*** (1962 to 1965)
    showing the interior of BARBIE® doll's first
    house. The house and furniture is constructed
    of paperboard.

86

87

88

86. *BARBIE®'s Dream House*
shown closed, with assembly
instruction book, and promotion
page advertising the house.
This was the first house
(1962 to 1965).
87. The front of *BARBIE®
Surprise House*.
88. *BARBIE® Dream Cottage* as
seen in the Mattel, Inc.
catalogue.
89. The interior of *BARBIE®
Country Living Home*.

89

91

92

93

94

90. The back yard and interior of the **BARBIE**®
    Surprise House. This house is hard to find and
    has many items.
91. Ken® doll could have been BARBIE® doll's
    architect for **The BARBIE® Magical Mansion**,
    if one notices the paperboard miniature house
    which came with this accessory. This unique
    and rare accessory is called *Ken® Playpack –
    Ken® At Work* c. 1993.
92. A fold-out advertisement for **The BARBIE®**
    Magical Mansion.
93. The exterior of the **BARBIE® Country**
    Living Home.
94. **BARBIE® Dream House** – yellow as seen in
    the Mattel, Inc. catalogue.

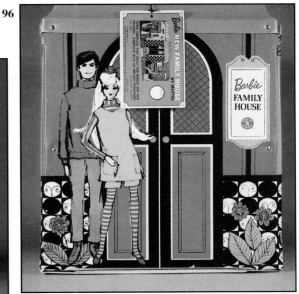

95. The interior of the **BARBIE® Family House** the tag shows the table and chairs in the bedroom and the bed in the entry way. This is incorrect. This house is correctly arranged in the 1967 fashion booklets.

96. **BARBIE® Family House** (1967) exterior with rare tag on the carrying handle.

97. The interior of the brightly colorful **BARBIE® Family Deluxe House"**. As one can see the mod furniture is of slightly smaller proportions to the **Color Magic BARBIE®** doll wearing "Fashion Editor".

98. **BARBIE® Family Deluxe House** is a 1966 Sears® exclusive house and also a carrying case. This rare house was made by Mattel, Inc.'s subsidiary SPP.

Chapter 6

BARBIE® DOLL HOME FURNISHINGS

As the popularity of BARBIE® doll grew, the accessories personified her lifestyle. If space did not permit a house, furniture could be purchased to create one's own settings.

Mattel, Inc. manufactured Danish Modern wood doll furniture in 1958 for 8in (20cm) to 10in (25cm) dolls. The pieces are identified with a stamp logo mark stating "MATTEL INTERNATIONAL," on the outer circumference of rim "JAPAN c. MCMLVIII". This Danish Modern furniture is adaptable for BARBIE® doll, Ken® doll, their family and friends. The furniture consisted of a sofa, easy chair, end table with lamp, studio set, buffet, dining table with chairs, queen size bed, and open wardrobe.

Suzy Goose Toys were under license from Mattel, Inc. to make doll furniture during the 1960s. They made beds, wardrobes, vanities with benches, chifforobes, pianos, hutches, and bunk beds. This furniture came in a variety of styles for BARBIE™ doll, Midge® doll, Ken® doll, Allen® doll, Skipper® doll, Francie® doll, Tutti® doll, and Todd® doll.

Mattel, Inc. introduced their line entitled *BARBIE® Go-Together Furniture!* in 1964. The line included the following:

>*Convertible Sofa-Bed with Coffee Table Kit*
>*Chair, Ottoman, & End Table Kit*
>*Chaise Lounge & Side Table Kit*
>*Lawn Swing & Planter Kit*

BARBIE® Go-Together Furniture Gift Set
This gift set included all of the furniture.

The 1965 line was called *BARBIE® 'N Skipper® Go-Together Furniture*. It featured the previous years furniture and new additions:.

>*Living Room Furniture Group*
>*Dining Room Furniture Kit*
>*Skipper®'s Double Bunk Beds*

The J.C. Penney® 1970, 1971, and 1972 Christmas catalogues offered the *Bedroom Suite*. It is a Suzy Goose Toys look-a-like. It is this author's hypothesis that it was manufactured using their similar canopy bed's headboard, vanity's mirror frame, telephone, and built in cosmetic tray. Perhaps Suzy Goose Toys had originally designed this *Bedroom Suite* for Skipper® doll, because the bed is too short for BARBIE® doll (her head touches the headboard and her feet hang over the footboard) and there are pictures of BARBIE® doll and Ken® doll on the vanity. The *Bedroom Suite* included a white canopy bed, yellow bedspread with lace trim, pillow-sham, matching canopy top, white vanity with vanity skirt, mirror, white telephone, white lamp with blue lamp shade, two picture silhouettes of BARBIE® doll and Ken® doll, and white vanity bench with yellow cloth seat. It should be noted that the author is the original owner of the *Bedroom Suite*. The J.C. Penney® catalog picture shows the matching vanity skirt and white lamp shade.

BARBIE® Dream House Finishing Touches were discovered on the shelves in 1985 at Kay-Bee® Toy Stores. There were three sets – *Kitchen Set, Bedroom Set,* and *Living Room Set*. They were produced for the 1982 market and had been stored in a warehouse for three years.

There has been several lines of furniture since 1980. The lines have included *BARBIE® Dream Furniture Collection* 1980 to 1984, *Dream Glow™ BARBIE® Furniture* 1986, *Sweet Roses™ BARBIE® Furniture* 1988, and *BARBIE® Pink Sparkles™* 1992.

The BARBIE® doll furniture has mirrored the popular designs and color schemes of interior decoration. As Mattel, Inc. continues to update, their BARBIE® doll furniture designs could be featured in any home-arama.

99

100

101

99. *BARBIE® Beauty Bath* (1976) was able to make real bubbles.

100. *BARBIE® Night Stand* (1983) was made under license by American Toy & Furniture Company, Inc. It measures 20in (51cm) x 16-1/2in (42cm) x 25in (64cm) high.

101. Suzy Goose Toys made BARBIE® doll furniture during the 1960's. The hutch on the left has a drawer which opens, the hutch on the right does not. The dolls are American Girl BARBIE® doll in "Dancing Doll" fashion and Skipper® doll with bendable legs in "Me 'N My Doll" fashion which includes the miniature BARBIE® doll.

102. The J.C. Penney® *Bedroom Suite* was offered in their catalogue in 1970, 1971, and 1972. It is rare. New Living Skipper® doll has her panda and is ready for bed in *Best Buy #3371*, 1972 pajamas.

102

103

104

105

106

103. **BARBIE® Dream Furniture – Desk & Seat** (1979).
104. **BARBIE® Dream Pool Collection – Patio Barbecue** (1979 to 1984).
105. *Pink Sparkles* (1991) BARBIE® doll's bedroom furniture.
106. **BARBIE® Dream Furniture Collection – Wicker-look Furniture** (1984) as shown in the Mattel, Inc. catalogue.
107. **BARBIE®'s Pool Party** (c. 1973) is a fun place for the Malibu dolls.

107

108

109

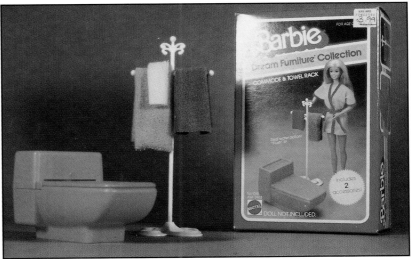

111

110

108. *BARBIE® Dream Furniture Collection – Vanity & Seat* (1979 to 1984).
109. *BARBIE® Dream Furniture Collection – Commode & Towel Rack* (1984). The commode flushes!
110. *BARBIE® Dream Furniture Collection – Dream Bed* (1984) as shown in the Mattel, Inc. catalogue.
111. *BARBIE® Dream House Finishing Touches* sets were *Kitchen Set* and *Bedroom Set*.
112. *Happy Birthday BARBIE® dolls* and *Gift Giving BARBIE® Doll* are having a Birthday party. The furniture is *BARBIE® Fashion Dining Room Set* (1984).

112

113. **BARBIE Bedroom Accents** (1987) is shown with *Dreamtime BARBIE doll & B.B.* (1985) – 'B.B.' stands for BARBIE doll's bear!

114. **BARBIE Bubbling Spa** (1984) as shown in the Mattel, Inc. catalogue.

115. *Pink Sparkles* (1991) showing the other pieces of BARBIE doll's furniture.

116. **BARBIE Action Accents** adorable wind-up toys, have been available since 1987.

Chapter 7

GROOVY VIBRATIONS AND MELODIES

BARBIE® doll, like songs, has been a reflection of the times. The groovy vibrations and melodies within this chapter have mirrored the times of BARBIE® doll, family and friends.

Mattel, Inc. distributed *BARBIE® Sings! (and Ken® doll too)* in 1961, a set of three 45 RPM records. The voice of BARBIE® doll was sung by Charlotte Austin and Ken® doll was sung by Bill Cunningham. The album consisted of six terrific tunes with words and music by Eliot Daniel and Ken Darby. They had been musical talent in Hollywood since 1939. Each had been Academy Award nominees; Ken Darby had won an Oscar for associate conducting on the 1956 musical film, "The King and I". Eliot Daniel wrote and scored the television show classic, "I Love Lucy" theme song.

Standard Plastic Products, Inc. Ponytail© made record totes in 1961. *BARBIE® Sings!,* Elvis Presley, The Beatles, Rickey Nelson, and Pat Boone (to name a few) records could be played on BARBIE® record players. Two companies manufactured BARBIE® record players – the 1962 Ememee Industries, Inc. and the 1963 Vanity Fair Record Player.

The 1964 *BARBIE® Ge-Tar*™ was a child-size musical toy guitar with patented musical unit. When you turned the crank it played "Bicycle Built For Two".

The Musical World of BARBIE® was the theme of six 33-1/3 RPM record albums in 1965, under license of Columbia Special Products (Columbia Records). Each 7in (18cm) album was a story and song adventure with BARBIE™ doll, Ken™ doll, Midge™ doll, Allen™ doll, Skipper™ doll, Skooter™ doll, and Ricky™ doll.

117

117. ***Let's Go To The Hop*** is an action musical by Enesco® Corporation. It has been an exclusive item from the moment of introduction.

The six record albums were as follows:

The World of BARBIE®
The Big Game
A Picnic For Skipper™
The BARBIE® Look
Skipper™, Skooter™ and Ricky™
A Happy BARBIE® Birthday

Donny and Marie Osmond T.V. Show Playset was manufactured in 1977 for BARBIE® doll acquaintances (they are not friends, nevertheless are important to BARBIE® doll documentation) "Donny Osmond doll" and "Marie Osmond doll". The popular teenage brother and sister singing artists had their own television variety show beginning in 1976 until 1978. In the television playset was a 33-1/3 RPM 7in (18cm) record of their song "We're Gettin' Together" c. 1976.

Kid Stuff produced under license a variety of musical compositions in 1981. A range that included disco, country, western, pop, and standards. The tunes with diversity were available as 33-1/3 RPM, long playing (LP's) records or cassette tapes.

The albums which were available are listed as follows:

BARBIE™ and Friends (record)
BARBIE™ Camping Adventure (record)
BARBIE™ Country Favorites (record and cassette)
BARBIE™ Dance Party (record and cassette)
BARBIE™ Birthday Album (record)
BARBIE™ and Her Friends (record)
BARBIE™ Christmas (record)

BARBIE™ and Her Friends was a limited edition record album. It was the most unique record in the series – both sides of the record have colorful illustrations of BARBIE® doll and her friends.

BARBIE® and The Rockers™ were a "Hot Rockin'™

118. ***Donny & Marie Osmond T.V. Show Playset.*** The popular singing artists had their own television variety show . **118**
As shown in this playset and on the television show, their younger brother Jimmy Osmond was a guest.

band in 1986 and 1987. Mattel, Inc. participated in the 1986 Macy's Thanksgiving Day Parade; riding on the float were BARBIE® and The Rockers™" (doll-impersonaters in people form). BARBIE® and The Rockers™ had *The Rockers™ Concert Stage, BARBIE® and The Rockers™ Video Recording Studio, Hot Rockin'™ Tour Van, The Rockers™ Dance Cafe,* and *BARBIE® and The Rockers™ Live Concert™ Instruments.* Plus BARBIE® and The Rockers™ had a promotional record. The record was a 6in (15cm) 33-1/3 RPM (a small size for this speed record) entitled *In Concert* c.1985. It was distributed free to those attending "BARBIE® On Tour" in Los Angeles, California.

The Beach Boys and the duet Jan & Dean recorded "Barbara Ann" in 1966. This song became a megahit and is one of the Beach Boys greatest hit singles. It was not made known until twenty years later (1986) that "Barbara Ann" was a tongue-in-cheek salute to the then seven year old popular BARBIE® doll. (This information is from "The Beach Boys-Sunkist-25th Anniversary Tour" concert exclusive album, c. 1986.)

In 1988, Mattel, Inc. introduced "California Dreamin'™ BARBIE® doll" (the name was later changed to "California BARBIE® doll") with a floppy vinyl record by The Beach Boys. The single was a tribute to a BARBIE® doll called "Living Doll".

Music videos became popular in the 1980's; not to be left-out, BARBIE® doll was in *tune.* Hi-Tops™ Video (A Division of Heron Communications, Inc.) released under license from Mattel, Inc. fully animated VHS video cassettes in two volumes. The videos featured two BARBIE® doll musical groups in each 25 minute video cassette tape. They were Volume 1 *BARBIE™ and The Rockers™ – Out of This World* c. 1987 and Volume 2 *BARBIE™ and The Sensations™ – Rockin' Back to Earth* c. 1987.

BARBIE® and The Beat the 1990, was a three member pop-rock band consisting of BARBIE® doll, her friends, Midge® doll and Christie® doll. The band and other Mattel, Inc. toys appeared in "Mattel, Inc. Kids Show", it was a nationwide tour. The 25 minute stage show debuted at Opryland Theme Park (a country music theme park) located in Nashville, Tennessee.

119

119.   The Enesco® Corporation advertisement for the musical figurines series, called the ***Glamour Collection***.

BARBIE® The Look c. 1990 Mattel, Inc. was manufactured and distributed by and under licensee Rhino Records, Inc. Included was the "Summit BARBIE® doll" commercial jingle, "Together We Can Do It (The World Song)". This expanded song version was performed by Shari Belafonte. The "Summit BARBIE® dolls" and Shari Belafonte were on the Mattel, Inc. float in the 1990 "Macy's Thanksgiving Day Parade".

Mattel, Inc. and the Walt Disney™ Company have long been associated in business. Beginning in 1955 Mattel, Inc. sponsored commercial breaks on the "Mickey Mouse Club".

Walt Disney World® (located in Florida) at Epcot® had a new show premier in late 1993 and revised in 1994 called, "The Magical World of BARBIE™". The show is sponsored by Mattel, Inc. There was a promotional 1¢ (with purchase) VHS video in Spring 1994 called *BARBIE® Birthday Party at Walt Disney World® -Epcot® '94.* The Magical World of BARBIE™ is entertaining for all ages as was evident to those of us attend-

120

ing Mattel, Inc. 1994 BARBIE® 35th Anniversary BARBIE™ Festival.

The Enesco® Corporation created under license for BARBIE® doll's 35th anniversary, *from BARBIE™ with Love* collection. The line included three musical figurines called the Glamour Collection. They were *Wedding Day 1959, Enchanted Evening 1960,* and *Solo In The Spotlight 1960.* The "Musical Memories" featured an action musical entitled, "Let's Go To The Hop". The musical is a record player with BARBIE® doll and Ken™ doll atop a revolving 45 Album twisting to "At The Hop".

BARBIE® doll has sung groovy vibrations and melodies on 45 RPM records, 33-1/3 RPM records, and videos. The changing musical sound waves of the past four decades have been represented in the BARBIE® doll music.

121

122

123

120. Columbia Records advertisement for their albums theme, "The Musical World of BARBIE®". American Girl BARBIE® doll is wearing *Dancing Doll.*
121. **BARBIE® Sings!** The first musical recording to feature BARBIE® doll and Ken® doll is hard to find. BARBIE® doll is wearing *Solo In the Spotlight* and Ken® doll is wearing *Tuxedo.*
122. **BARBIE® The Look** (c. 1990).
123. BARBIE® doll's friend Steffie® doll keeps time like the beat of a metrotone. The **Tomy** grand piano has wind-up music box on the seat of the chair.

124

125

126

127

128

124. "Barbara Ann" was recorded in 1966 by The Beach Boys and duet Jan & Dean as a tongue-in-cheek salute to BARBIE® doll.

125. *Kid Stuff records* shown on the left is the limited edition *BARBIE™ and Her Friends,* a unique picture record – hard to find. Shown on the right is *BARBIE® Birthday Album.*

126. The very rare **BARBIE® Electronic Piano** (c. 1982) uses a 9-volt alkaline battery. One can, using the wands and songbook, play "BARBIE® Doll Song" (based on the 1966 song "Georgy Girl"). Pink 'N Pretty BARBIE® doll was not included.

127. The Enesco® Corporation 1994 promotionals *from BARBIE™ with Love collection booklet and button*.

128. **BARBIE® and The Rockers™ record** was called *"In Concert"* c. 1985. The 33-1/3 RPM record was distributed free to those attending "BARBIE® On Tour" in Los Angeles, California.

129

130

131

132

129. ***BARBIE® and The Rockers™ Live Concert Instruments.***
130. The Child World/Children's Palace 1989 exclusive, BARBIE® Dance Club doll came with a tape player with microphone and ***BARBIE® Dance Club Cassette***.
131. BARBIE® and The Sensations™ are bee-bopping in the ***BARBIE® and the Sensations™ Jukebox Music Shop*** (1988). The dolls are BARBIE® doll, Becky® doll, Bobsy® doll, Belinda® doll and Bobby BiBobs™ (a.k.a. Ken® doll in Germany).
132. California Dreamin'™ BARBIE® doll came with the floppy vinyl record, "***Living Doll***" by The Beach Boys.

133. The VHS video cassettes were Volume 1 **BARBIE® and The Rockers™ – Out of This World** c. 1987 and Volume 2 **BARBIE® and The Sensations™ – Rockin' Back to Earth** c. 1987. Each are hard to find.

134. **BARBIE® and The Beat "Dance Cafe"** c. 1990, was distributed in the United States. The cover shows Bobby BiBobs™ (available 1988 in Germany.)

135. **BARBIE® Ice Capades 50th Anniversary Skating Rink** c. 1989 is hard to find.

136. **BARBIE® for Girls Cassette Player with Headset and Microphone** (c. 1993) by Kiddesigns, Inc.

137

138

139

137. The theme of 50th Anniversary Ice Capade tour was the **Exclusive Live Tour of BARBIE**™.

138. FAO Schwarz special limited edition **Rockette**™ **BARBIE**® **doll** (1993). A handful were autographed by the Radio City Music Hall Rockettes at the date of premiere. Also shown is the **BARBIE**® **Festival Autograph Card** signed by Ann Driskill, the doll's costume designer.

139. The advertisement for the Spring 1994 promotional 1¢ VHS video called, "BARBIE® Birthday Party at Walt Disney World® – Epcot® '94". The "Disney Fun BARBIE™ doll" is exclusive to the Disney® theme parks.

140. **BABRIE**™ **Solo in the Spotlight Telephone** was a 1995 limited edition created and designed by M. H. Segan L. P. , distributed by Kash 'N' Gold Ltd. The BARBIE™ doll figure is made of cold cast porcelain and when this unique telephone rings the song "Busy Buzz" plays. This catchy tune was orignally on the "BARBIE™ Sings!" record album. This is sure to be a desirable item in the future.

140

Chapter 8

WINNING GAMES

Games are a form of entertainment involving strategy and chance. Usually, one's mental picture of a game is that of a board game played by two or more persons by rolling a die and strategically moving playing pieces until a player reaches completion and is declared the winner.

Mattel, Inc. rolled the die in 1961 with the release of the first game and BARBIE doll has been winning games ever since. New technology 29 years later (1992) brought video and computer games. The following games have been either produced by Mattel, Inc. or have been under license.

1961   *The BARBIE Game – Queen of the Prom* board game made by Mattel, Inc.

1963   *BARBIE Queen of the Prom Game* board game made by Mattel, Inc. This game is a revised issue of the 1961 game.

1963   *BARBIE Keys To Fame Game* board game by Mattel, Inc.

1964   *BARBIE 's Little Sister Skipper Game* board game by Mattel, Inc.

1967   *The BARBIE World of Fashion Game* board game by Mattel, Inc.

1970   *Miss Lively Livin' BARBIE Game* board game by Mattel, Inc.

1979   *BARBIE Plastic Coated Playing Cards* playing cards by Nasta, Inc.

1980   *The BARBIE Game* board game by Whitman – Western Publishing Company, Inc.

1986   *BARBIE Charms the World Game* board game by Mattel, Inc.

1986   *BARBIE We Girls Can Do Anything Game* board game by Golden – Western Publishing Company, Inc.

1990   *BARBIE Just Us Girls* board game by Cardinal, Inc.

1991   *BARBIE Queen of the Prom – 1990's Edition Game* board game by Golden – Western Publishing Company, Inc.

1991   *BARBIE Shopping Spree – Giant Card Game* card game by Golden – Western Publishing Company, Inc.

1992   *BARBIE For Girls Travel Games Series: "Cool Jobs"; "Ultimate Vacation"; "Pretty Party"* board games by International Games – A Mattel, Inc. Company

1992   *BARBIE We Girls Can Do Anything Game* board game by Golden – Western Publishing Company, Inc. This game is a reissue of the 1986 game having the same name.

1992   *BARBIE Dream Date* board game by Golden – Western Publishing Company, Inc.

1992   *Dress Up BARBIE Game* board game by Colorforms, Inc.

141

141.   The first BARBIE doll game was T*he BARBIE Game – Queen of the Prom* in 1961, made by Mattel, Inc. Whitman Publishing Company issued a reproduction of this same game in 1994.

142

143

144

145

1992 *BARBIE™ A Glamorous Quest Full of Magic Fun and Adventure* video game by Hi Tech Expressions Entertainment and distributed by Nintendo Entertainment System® – Nintendo of America, Inc.

1992 *BARBIE™ Game Girl* video game by Hi Tech Expressions Entertainment and distributed by Nintendo Game Boy® – Nintendo of America, Inc.

1992 *BARBIE® A Glamorous Quest Full of Magic Fun and Adventure* computer game by Hi Tech Expressions Entertainment.

1994 *BARBIE™ Vacation Adventure"* video game by Hi Tech Expressions Entertainment. This was distributed by both Super Nintendo® – Nintendo of America, Inc. and Sega™ Genesis™ – Sega Enterprises, Ltd.

1994 *BARBIE™ and Her Magical Home* CD-ROM game by Hi Tech Expressions

1994 *BARBIE™ Super Model* video game and computer game by Sega Enterprises, Ltd.

1994 The *BARBIE® Game - Queen of the Prom - 35th Anniversary Edition* board game by Golden-Western Publishing.

1995 *POG Fun BARBIE® Doll* by Mattel, Inc. an official licensed product of The World POG Federation.

1995 *BARBIE® Dress Up Game* board game by International Games, Inc. A Mattel Company.

1995 *BARBIE® Butterfly Princess Game* board game by International Games, Inc. A Mattel, Inc. Company.

142. *The BARBIE™ Game* c. 1980 by Whitman® – Western Publishing Company, Inc.

143. *BARBIE® Charms the World® Game* c. 1986 by Mattel, Inc.

144. BARBIE® doll entered the computer age with information systems. *BARBIE® A Glamorous Quest Full of Magic Fun and Adventure* c. 1992 by Hi-Tech Expressions Entertainment.

145. *BARBIE® Little Sister, Skipper® Game* is a 1964 board game by Mattel, Inc. This is a rare and hard to find game. The photo-art on the box lid is like horse farms in the author's home state of Kentucky.

146

147

148

149

150

146. **BARBIE® Queen of the Prom – 1990's Edition Game** c. 1991 by Golden® – Western Publishing Company, Inc.
147. **BARBIE® Shopping Spree – Giant Card Game** c. 1991 by Golden™ – Western Publishing Company, Inc.
148. **BARBIE® For Girls Travel Game Series** c. 1992 by International Games – A Mattel, Inc. Company.
149. **BARBIE™ Dream Date** c. 1992 by Golden® – Western Publishing, Inc.
150. **BARBIE™ Plastic Coated Playing Cards** c. 1979 by Nasta, Inc.

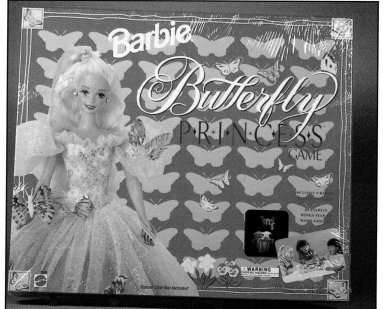

151

152

153

154

151. **BARBIE® Butterfly Princess™ Game** c. 1995 International Games, Inc., a Mattel, Inc. Company.
152. **POG™ Fun BARBIE® Doll** c. 1955 is an official licensed product of "The World of Pog Federation". POG is based on the milkcap game of years past.
153. The **BARBIE™ Game – Queen of the Prom – 35th Anniversary Edition** c. 1994 was produced by Golden-Western Publishing Company, Inc. Hard to find.
154. **BARBIE® Dress Up Game** c. 1995 International Games, Inc., A Mattel, Inc. Company.

Chapter 9

TRANSPORTATION – WHEELS, WINGS, AND SPEED BOATS

BARBIE® doll and Ken® doll have been dashing around and spinning their wheels on their vehicles on Route 66 since 1962. BARBIE® doll and Ken® doll cars have never been beat, cruising the strip on Friday and Saturday night dates.

Irwin Corporation under license from Mattel, Inc. begin manufacturing transportation wares in 1962. They made the following automobiles, boats and an airplane:

BARBIE®'s Sports Car 1962 to 1964. This car is an Austin Healy and came in a variety of colors – coral (some have aged to a salmon or peach), lavender, turquoise, red, and beige.

BARBIE® and *Ken® Hot Rod* 1963 to 1964. This hot rod came in two colors, turquoise and red.

BARBIE®, Ken®, Midge®, and Allen® Corvette 1964 to 1965. This came in blue.

Allen®'s Roadster 1964. This car was an aqua Mercedes-Benz.

BARBIE® Sports Plane 1964.

BARBIE® and *Skipper's Speed Boat* 1964.

Mattel, Inc. has marketed multitudinous mobile transportation in various makes and models. BARBIE® doll and Ken™ doll have flown the friendly skies with *United Airlines on BARBIE®'s Friend Ship*. There have been bicycles, motor-scooters, recreational vehicles, and boats.

The highlights of transportation designed during the past three and one-half decades are illustrated.

155

155. *BARBIE® Ferrari* (1988).

156

157

158

156. Through the years BARBIE® doll has put the pedal to the medal in an assortment of luxury sports cars.

157. *United Airlines BARBIE® Friend Ship* (1973 to 1977) came with BARBIE® doll size stewardess smock, mobil serving cart, suitcase, serving tray, coffee pot with lid, two coffee cups, two saucers, and two beverage glasses. This accessory is very rare to locate with all the pieces.

158. *BARBIE®'s Beach Bus* (1974 to 1977) was a fun way to go to the beach in Malibu.

159

160

161

159. *BARBIE® Travelin' Trailer/Off-Road Vehicle and Horse Trailer* (1983) was a Department Store Special.
160. *BARBIE®'s Ten Speeder* (1974 to 1977) had real bike features! The wheels turn and the kickstand swings up and down.
161. *BARBIE®'s Classy Corvette* (1976) was a Department Store Special.
162. *SuperStar Barbie's Star "Vette"* (1977 to 1979).

162

163

164

165

163. ***Ken® Dream "Vette"*** (1985) was a Toys R Us exclusive. It is rare and hard to find.
164. ***BARBIE® '57 Chevy*** (1989). This sky-blue Chevrolet Bel-Air is hard to find.
165. ***BARBIE® Around Town Scooter*** (c. 1992).

166

167

168

166. *BARBIE® Porsche 911 Cabriolet* (c. 1993).
167. *Camp BARBIE® Sun Cruiser* (1994).
168. *BARBIE® Ford Mustang* (c. 1993).

169

170

171

172

169. *Swim 'N Dive BARBIE® Speedboat* (1994).
170. Ken® doll has hydro-plained the ocean waves in the *Swim 'N Dive BARBIE™ Speedboat* and *Swim 'N Dive BARBIE™ doll* has decided to go scuba diving.
171. *BARBIE® Jaguar XJS* (1994).
172. *BARBIE® Sports Car* was BARBIE® doll's first car. It was an Austin Healy and had a personalized plate.

174

175

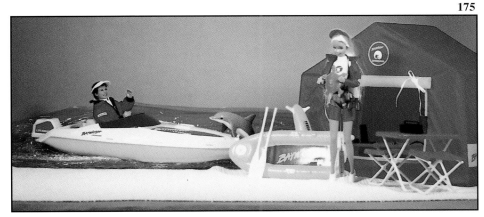

176

177

173. **BARBIE® doll Mustang** (1995). The Mustang trademark was used under license from Ford Motor Company. This BARBIE® doll automobile expands from a two seater to a four seater.

174. **Baywatch BARBIE® Remote Control Rescue Cruiser** c. 1995.

175. "Baywatch" is a popluar television show in the United States and in the European countries. BARBIE® doll and Ken® doll are on the scene, "Baywatch Ken® doll steering the **BARBIE® Rescue Boat** (1995) and *Baywatch BARBIE® doll* is at the **Baywatch BARBIE® Rescue Station** (1995).

176. The internationally famous television show, "Baywatch" is popular BARBIE® doll accessories. The **Baywatch BARBIE® Rescue Wheels** (1995) and *Baywatch BARBIE® Rescue Station*, 1995.

177. **The BARBIE® Sports Cruiser** (1995) is a 4 x 4 vehicle and casually chic is the FAO Schwarz exclusive, "Shopping Spree BARBIE® doll" with her shopping bag.

Chapter 10

SCENE PRESENTATION

An important aspect to the world of BARBIE® doll, Ken® doll, Skipper® doll, family and friends is for their owners, either child or collector, to play-act. The BARBIE® doll was created to have *fun* with and not be a nest-egg.

This author has happy childhood recollections of BARBIE® doll playing and the transition into becoming a collector. I am an everything BARBIE® doll collector, (yes, although not the subject of this book, I do collect the dolls and fashions) I also enjoy the scene presentation as representation of life-like situations.

Incalculable accessories have taken the dolls through life-like adventures and activities: school, careers, shopping, and dining. Each has been the scenery in the play-act world of BARBIE® doll.

These accessories were made from paperboard and are listed as follows:

1962 to 1964 *BARBIE® Fashion Shop*
1964 *BARBIE® and Ken® Little Theatre*

1964 to 1965 *BARBIE® Goes To College,* a Sears® exclusive
1965 *BARBIE® and Skipper® School*
1966 *BARBIE® and Francie® Campus,* a Sears® exclusive
1971 *BARBIE® Fashion Stage*

The following settings were either made of vinyl, fiberboard, plastic, or combination:

1971 *BARBIE® Cafe Today*
1971 *BARBIE® Town and Country Market*
1971 *BARBIE® Boutique*
1973 *Quick Curl Boutique*
1975 *BARBIE® Olympic Ski Village*
1975 *BARBIE® and P.J. Olympic Gymnast*
1976 to 1977 *BARBIE® Fashion Plaza*
1976 to 1977 *Ballerina BARBIE® Stage,* a Sears® exclusive

178. **BARBIE® Dream Store – Fashion Department** (1982 to 1984).

178

1977 to 1979 *SuperStar BARBIE® Photo Studio,* a Sears® exclusive

1978 to 1979 *SuperStar BARBIE® Stage Show*

1982 to 1984 *BARBIE® Dream Store – Fashion Department*

1982 to 1984 *BARBIE® Dream Store – Makeup Department*

1985 *BARBIE® Home and Office.* This was Day-To-Night BARBIE® doll's YUPPIE office which was covered in the press.

1986 to 1987 *Great Shape BARBIE® Workout Center*

1987 *BARBIE® Six O'Clock News*

1988 *BARBIE® Step 'N Style Boutique*

1988 *BARBIE® Island Fun Hut*

1988 *California Dreamin' BARBIE® Hot Dog Stand*

1988 *California Dreamin' BARBIE® Surf 'N Shop*

1990 *All-American BARBIE® Hamburger Stand*

1990 *BARBIE® Flight Time Airport*

1990 *BARBIE® All-Stars Sports Club*

1994 *BARBIE® Supermarket*

1994 *BARBIE® Baby Care Center*

1994 *BARBIE® Post Office*

There have been play packs and numerous items that make wonderful make-believe scenes.

179

180

179. BARBIE® dolls and Midge® dolls are in attendance for the fashion show being held today at the ***BARBIE® Fashion Shop*** (1962 to 1964).

180. Storyboards from ***BARBIE® and Ken® Little Theatre*** were found in a warehouse, circa 1991.

181

182

181. *BARBIE®*
Olympic Ski
Village (1975).
182. Mattel, Inc.'s
Sweetheart
Park (1975) is
rare. It is the
correct scale for
BARBIE® doll,
although it was
made for the
Sweetheart
Dolls.
183. *BARBIE®*
Fashion Plaza
(1976 to 1977).
This shopping
mall has work-
ing escalator,
when the string
is pulled,
BARBIE® doll
can go up.

183

184

185

186

184. *SuperStar BARBIE®*
Photo Studio (1978 to
1979) was a
Sears® exclusive.

185. *SuperStar BARBIE®*
Photo Studio photo-
graphic equipment
could be stored inside.

186. *SuperStar BARBIE®*
Photo Studio was a
modeling studio for
SuperStar BARBIE® and
SuperStar Ken®.

187

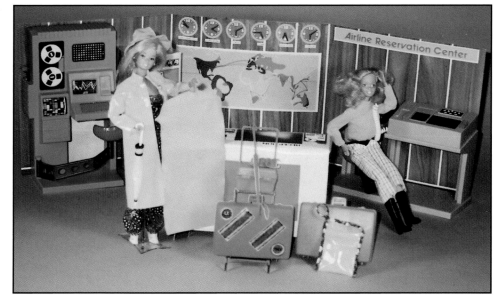

188

189

187. Sears® exclusive *Reservation Center* (1978 to 1980) and *Play Pak® – Get Aways* (1978) luggage.
188. BARBIE® doll and Skipper® doll are in the woods with various animals. The tent, backpack, etc. is *Play Pak – Campin' Out* (1980).
189. *BARBIE® Dream Store – Make-Up Department* (1982 to 1984).

190

191

192

190. *Play Paks – Western Round Up* (1981) and *Play Pak – Horseback Riding* (1980).

191. *Tracy® & Todd® Wedding Play Pak* (1984).

192. *Great Shape BARBIE® Workout Center* (1986 to 1987).

193. *Dinner Date* (1985) has miniature menus, food, dishes, salad bar, table, chairs, diorama, dance floor, etc. It is very creative and hard to find. (made by Arco, a Mattel, Inc. company).

193

194

195

196

194. **BARBIE® Six O'Clock News** (1987) – Hard to find.

195. **BARBIE® Step 'N Style Boutique** (1988) has many authentic-like shoe store fixtures, such as the setting-stool and the brannock device to measure the foot size.

196. The Department Store Specials, Hawaiian BARBIE® dolls and Hawaiian Ken® dolls look adorable with the **BARBIE® Island Fun Hut** (1988).

197

198

199

197. *BARBIE® Supermarket* (1994).
198. *All-American BARBIE™ Hamburger Stand* (1990), All-American BARBIE™ doll and All-American Ken™ doll are wearing their Reebok foot wear.
199. The California Dreamin'™ Dolls with the *California Dreamin'™ Surf 'N Shop, California Dreamin'™ Beach Taxi,* and *California Dreamin'™ Hot Dog Stand*. (It is designed like a hot dog). (1988)

200

201

202

200. *Hollywood Hair BARBIE®
    Beauty Center* (1992).
201. The *BARBIE® & Ken® Little
    Theatre* exterior has graphics
    depicting the masks of
    comedy and tragedy, show
    poster, and ticket window.
    Hard to find.
202. *BARBIE® Post Office* (1994).

203

204

203. ***BARBIE® Baby Care Center*** (1994).

204. ***BARBIE® Pretty Treasurers***™ 1995. Each set is excellent quality and economical.

205. Two ways to skate – in-line skating and ice skating! ***Hot Skatin' BARBIE® doll 2-in-1 Skatin' Fun*** (1995, accessory).

205

206

208

207

206. *BARBIE® Magic Moves Home Office* (1995).
207. The interior of the *BARBIE® and Ken® Little Theatre (1964)* has a working fabric curtain, props, three reversible background scenes and a booklet containing seven play scripts.
208. *BARBIE® Picnic Set* c. 1992 with the hard to find BARBIE® doll logo cooler.

Chapter 11

THE PET MENAGERIE

BARBIE® doll's pet menagerie has comprised many species of the animal kingdom. The pets have their own branch on the BARBIE® doll family tree. BARBIE® doll has had thirteen horses and could have her own horse farm in the Bluegrass State (author's home state of Kentucky). She has had three cats and kittens. Not quite enough for nine lives but a meow mix none-the-less. A growling (pun intended) collection of five dogs and puppies. Furthermore there have been three exotic animals.

The pets in the United States have included the following:

HORSES

> 1971   *Dancer*™
> 1981-1984   *Dallas*™ *Golden Palomino*
> 1982-1984   *Midnight*™ *Stallion*
> 1983   *Honey*™, *Skipper*® *doll's pony*
> 1984   *Dixie*™ *Palomino colt*
>   (off-spring mare of *Dallas*™ and *Midnight*™)
> 1988   *Prancer*™ *Arabian Stallion*
> 1988   *Blinking Beauty*™
> 1990   *Sun Runner*™
> 1991   *All-American*™
> 1991   *Snow Flake*™
> 1992   *Rosebud*™
> 1993   *Western Star*™
> 1994 to 1995   *High Stepper*™

CATS and KITTENS

> 1983   *Fluff*™ *Kitten*
> 1992   *Honey*™ *Kitten*
> 1994   *Mitzi Meow*™ *Cat*

DOGS and PUPPIES

> 1980   *Beauty*™ *Afghan Hound*
> 1981   *Beauty*™ *and Puppies Afghan*
>   *Hound family*
> 1985   *Prince*™ *French Poodle*
> 1992   *Sachi*™ *Puppy*
> 1994   *Puppy Ruff*™ *Puppy*

209

209.   ***Parisian BARBIE***™ from France (1980 to 1984, *first issue* in the *BARBIE*® *Doll International Series*) is taking her French poodle for a walk in Paris.

EXOTIC ANIMALS

> 1986   *Tahiti*™ *Tropical Bird*
> 1989   *Zizi*™ *Zebra*
> 1989   *Ginger*™ *Giraffe*

210

211

212

210. The *BARBIE® doll Family Tree* is frequently up-dated. All family, friends and pets are listed.
211. The Afghan Hound family, *Beauty™ and Puppies* (1981) – hard to find.
212. A western horse ranch. The horses are *Dixie™*, *Honey™*, and *Midnight™*.

213

214

215

216

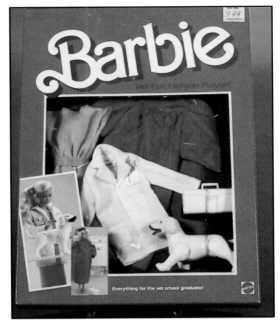

213. The *Afghan Hound family* was illustrated on a c. 1982, Mattel, Inc. trading card.
214. The precious little kitten is *Fluff*™ (1983) – rare.
215. *High Stepper Horse* (1994) really walks (with batteries). Top seller for the Christmas season, 1994.
216. *BARBIE® Vet Fun Fashion Playset* c. 1984 – hard to find.
217. *Prince*™ (1985) a French Poodle – hard to find.

217

218

220

219

221

218. *Puppy Ruff*™ (1994) barks and *Mitzi Meow* (1994) meows.
219. *BARBIE*® *Pretty Pet Parlor* (1994) is a pet store.
220. *Tahati*™ (1988) a Tropical Bird – hard to find.
221. *Blinking Beauty*™ (1988).

Chapter 12

THE TOY CHEST

Toy is a Scandinavian word meaning little tool. In essence a toy is a light-hearted aspect a child uses to learn about the world. Generations of children have kept their childhood treasures in the toy chest.

Innumerable BARBIE® doll toys have been manufactured by Mattel, Inc. and produced under license. Among the unique are: View-Master, ColorForms, and Miniature Collectibles.

View-Master has been a subsidiary of various companies through the years because the parent companies went out-of-business. View-Master reels are three-dimensional stero pictures. The View-Master listing is as follows:

Sawyer's – *BARBIE® Around The World Trip* c.1965

GAF – *BARBIE® Around The World Trip* c.1965

GAF – *BARBIE®'s Great American Photo Race* c. 1973

GAF – Talking View-Master *BARBIE®'s Around The World Trip* c. 1965. It was on the retail shelves in 1974 and shortly after being released, was recalled.

GAF – Talking View-Master *BARBIE®'s Great American Photo Race* c. 1973. It was available during 1974.

GAF – *SuperStar BARBIE*™ c. 1978

View-Master – *BARBIE® and The Rockers*™ c. 1986

View-Master – *BARBIE® and The Rockers*™ *Go On Tour* Gift Set c. 1986. This gift set included the BARBIE™ and The Rockers™ reels and a View-Master.

View-Master – *BARBIE*™ – *Featuring SuperStar BARBIE®* c. 1989

ColorForms has consecutively produced a new under license BARBIE® doll theme since 1970. Mattel, Inc. provides ColorForms with BARBIE® doll photo art and transparencies to ensure accuracy. The following ColorForms have been available:

BARBIE® Dress-Up Kit 1970

BARBIE® 3-D Fashion Theatre 1972

Malibu BARBIE® 1972

BARBIE® Sport Fashion Set 1975

BARBIE® Lace & Dress Dancing Doll 1975

222

222. ***BARBIE® Dress-Up Kit*** (1970) was made by ColorForms with *Velvet Venture* as one of the plastic fashions in the set and shown on the dress form. The doll and photo art paperboard doll is, Dramatic New Living BARBIE® doll".

223

BARBIE® *Dress-Up* 1977
Ballerina BARBIE™ 1977
SuperStar BARBIE™ 1977
The BARBIE® Dream House™ *Play Set* 1979
BARBIE® *Dress-Up Set* 1979
BARBIE® *and Beauty*™ *Dress-Up Set* 1981
Western BARBIE™ *Dress-Up Set* 1982
BARBIE® *Dress-Up Set* 1984
Great Shape BARBIE® Dress-Up Set 1984
BARBIE® *and the Sensations*™ 1988
BARBIE® *Magical Mansion*™ 1990
BARBIE® *Fashion Boutique Play Set* 1992
Costume Ball BARBIE™ 1992
Hollywood Hair BARBIE™ 1992
Secret Hearts BARBIE™ 1993
Glitter Hair BARBIE™ 1994
Camp BARBIE™ *Play Set* 1994
Baywatch BARBIE™ *Play Set* 1995

Arco Toys Ltd. a Mattel, Inc. company, manufactured two series of miniature collectibles called, "Forever BARBIE™ Miniature Collectibles" c. 1989 and "Miniature BARBIE™ Collectibles" c. 1990. Each series contains six miniature collectibles. They were as follows:

Forever BARBIE® Miniature Collectibles
  c. 1989
Wedding Party BARBIE™ 1959

224

225

223. Power Wheels designed many battery operated child-size BARBIE® doll themed sports cars.
224. Ken® doll underwear, ***Hanes make Ken® feel good all under*** c. 1980, made by Mattel, Inc. It was on the market for a short time, before becoming a generic.
225. ***Baywatch BARBIE® doll,*** 1995 made under license by ColorForms.

Solo in the Spotlight BARBIE™ *1959*
Evening Enchantment BARBIE™ *1959*
California Dream BARBIE™ *1988*
Happy Holidays BARBIE™ *1988*
SuperStar BARBIE™ *1989*

This series has several faux pas. *Wedding Party BARBIE*™ *1959* is **Wedding Day Set 1959.** The incorrect year (1959) of issue is given for *Solo in the Spotlight BARBIE*™, it was 1960. *Evening Enchantment BARBIE*™ *1959* should be **Enchanted Evening BARBIE**™ **1960.** *Happy Holidays BARBIE*™ *1988* has the incorrect date, the correct date is 1989.

226

Miniature BARBIE™ *Collectibles* c.1990
BARBIE™ *1959*
Sensations BARBIE™ *1988*
Dance Club BARBIE™ *1989*
Cool Times BARBIE™ *1989*
Beach Blast BARBIE™ *1989*
Ballerina BARBIE™ *1989*

The error in this series is the claim that *BARBIE*™ *1959* has a beach towel; the 1959 editions did not come with beach towels.

Even though these series have inaccuracies they are distinct. They were hard to locate at the time of issue in some parts of the United States.

Throughout the years there has been a variety of BARBIE® doll toy merchandise. Previously mentioned and illustrated are unique toys found in the toy chest.

227

226. ColorForms has produced **BARBIE® Notebook Transfers** (c. 1990).
227. **Dance! Workout with BARBIE®** (1992) was approved by the Aerobics & Fitness Association of America.
228. The GAF – Talking View-Master with GAF – Talking View-Master Reels, **BARBIE®'s Around The World Trip** c. 1965. It was on the retail shelves in 1974 and shortly thereafter, recalled – very rare and hard to find.

228

229

230

231

229. GAF – Talking View-Master Reels,
     ***BARBIE®'s Great American Photo
     Race*** c. 1973 (was available in 1974)
     with The GAF – Talking View-Master
     – rare and hard to find.
230 GAF – ***SuperStar BARBIE***™ c. 1978
     reels.
231. ColorForms has produced a new theme
     consecutively since 1970.

232

233

234

232. Farrow Industries marketed in miniature the 1981 BARBIE® doll line. Hard to find.

233. *Forever BARBIE™ Miniature Collectibles* (c. 1989) series.

234. *BARBIE® and The Rockers™ Go On Tour*, View-Master Gift Set (c. 1986).

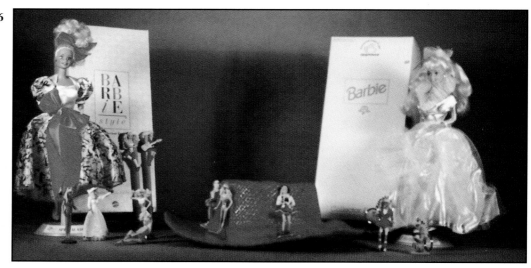

235. *Miniature BARBIE™ Collectibles* (c. 1990) series.
236. Applause, Inc. distributed a variety of BARBIE® doll items in 1990 and 1991. The hat was created by the author using the BARBIE® doll figurines.
237. *BARBIE® Dress-Up Sets* travel paks by ColorForms.

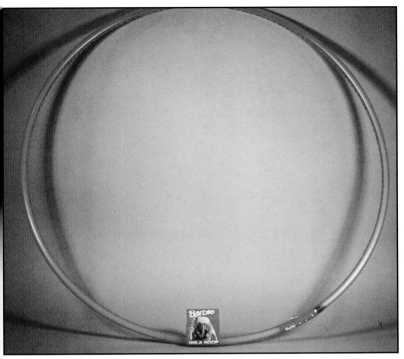

238

239

240

241

242

238. **BARBIE Hula Hoop**
(1991) by Wham-O.
239. **BARBIE YoYo** (1990) by
Spectra Star.
240. The tag on the **BARBIE
Hula Hoop** (1991) by
Wham-O.
241. **BARBIE for Girls –
Sky Master 700 Series
Kite** (1994) by
Spectra Star.
242. **Flying BARBIE Disc**
(1990) by Spectra Star.

Chapter 13

CREATIVITY – SEWING, KNITTING AND ARTS & CRAFTS

An assortment of BARBIE® doll products have enabled the child to learn to sew, knit, and paint. If someone enjoys these things as a hobby, then they can appreciate the thought which went into teaching a child with these products. Each has had easy-to-follow directions.

The BARBIE™ doll commercial pattern has been made since 1961 by Advance Pattern Company of New York. Stitches in time (through the years) commercial patterns have been designed for BARBIE® doll, family and friends. They have been produced and distributed by McCalls, Simplicity, Butterick, and Advance. These patterns were designed for the young seamstress to learn by clearly explained step-by-step basic sewing techniques.

Miner Industries, Inc. *Knitting For BARBIE®* was under license from Mattel, Inc. in 1962. Their knitting kits with plastic knitting needles, virgin wool yarn, and illustrated step-by-step instructions were especially designed for young beginners. The following four patterns were available:

> *Two Piece Skating Outfit* (This was a sweater and slacks outfit)
> *Skirt and Sleeveless Blouse*
> *Fitted Coat and Pill Box Hat*
> *Sleeveless Dress and Stole*

The Fashion Embroidery Set produced by Standard Toy Kraft in 1962 featured cloth doll figures, fabric with costume designs and an embroidery kit. The following three sets were available:

> *BARBIE® Fashion Embroidery Set*
> *BARBIE® and Ken® Fashion Embroidery Set*
> *BARBIE®, Ken® and Skipper® Fashion Embroidery Set*
> *Skipper® Fashion Embroidery Set* was available in 1965.

Mattel, Inc. introduced *BARBIE®'s Sew-Free® Fashion-Fun Costumes* in 1965. This was an innovative way to make BARBIE® doll clothes without sewing – by measuring and cutting the "Sew-Free Strips" (which had a sticky backing), cutting the pattern, and pressing the edges together on the "Sew-Free Strips". The costume would permanently stay together. There were twelve costumes and they were as follows:

> *From Nine To Five*
> *Sorority Tea*
> *Pretty Traveler*
> *Hootenanny*
> *Patio Party*
> *Debutante Party*
> *Day In Town*
> *Sightseeing*
> *Moonlight 'N Roses*
> *Stardust*
> *Day 'N Night*
> *Golden Ball*

The BARBIE™ doll Fashion Maker (1981) allowed one to create their own BARBIE® doll fashions from twelve pattern pieces. This set had hundreds of design possibilities.

The *BARBIE™ Touch 'N Color Artist Revolving Carousel* was manufactured under license in 1983. The carousel had materials for the budding artist to experiment with various mediums on a revolving plastic tray. It included water colors, crayons, tempera paints, non-toxic markers and other art supplies.

A vast majority of people enjoy sewing, knitting, and the arts and crafts.

243

244

245

243. ***Knitting For BARBIE*®**
(1962) – BARBIE® doll is
wearing *Sweater Girl*
fashion. Hard to find.
244. ***BARBIE*® *Color By***
Number (c. 1962) was
designed by Whitman®
Publishing Company – Rare.
245. ColorForms has made a
variety of ***BARBIE*®**
Shrinky Dink Sets. This
shown set is c. 1983.
246. *McCall's* has produced and
distributed many patterns.
The two-page advertisement
was from their November
1963 magazine issue.

246

247

248

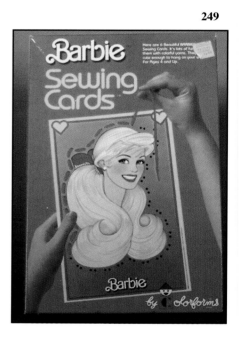

249

250

247. ***BARBIE®'s Electric Drawing Set*** (c. 1963) by Lakeside Toys. The concept was to teach children basic drawing techniques by tracing. Hard to find.

248. Craft House has distributed ***BARBIE® Glitter Paint By Number*** each is c. 1994.

249. ***BARBIE® Sewing Cards*** have been in assorted themes and have been produced by ColorForms. This item is c. 1988.

250. ***Sew-Free Fashion-Fun*** pattern entitled, "Hootenanny" c. 1963. These patterns are very hard to find.

251

253

254

251. The Mattel, Inc. **BARBIE® Fashion Decorator™ System** c. 1993.
252. **BARBIE™ Jewelry Holder** c. 1994 by Craft House.
253. **BARBIE® Rub and Color** c. 1989 was by Craft House.
254. **BARBIE™ Sand Fun** c. 1994 is basically a color-by-numbers using sand
   to create pictures.

Chapter 14

FUN ACTIVITIES

The instanteous popularity of BARBIE® doll expanded into fun activities. These miscellaneous wares - coloring books, jigsaw puzzles, and trading cards – were made by Mattel, Inc. and under license.

Western Publishing Company, Inc. published the first BARBIE® doll coloring book (1962), *BARBIE® and Ken® Coloring Book* with drawings by Al Anderson and Nathalee Mode. They have printed all coloring books and coloring books with paper dolls in various themes featuring BARBIE® doll, Ken® doll, family, friends, and items in the line.

Whitman Publishing Company, a division of Western Publishing Company, Inc., has printed unique jigsaw puzzles and frame-tray puzzles with BARBIE™ doll, Ken™ doll, Skipper™ doll, Midge™ doll, Skooter® doll, and other friends.

Trading Card Sets have been produced five times during the years. The Dynamic Toy Company designed two illustrated sets in 1962. They were *BARBIE® Jumbo Trading Cards* and *BARBIE™ and Ken™ Jumbo Trading Cards.* Each set consisted of 35 cards. The *BARBIE™ Jumbo Trading Cards* were numbered from 141 to 175. The *BARBIE™ and Ken™ Jumbo Trading Cards* were numbered from 176 to 210. These were large cards measuring 3-1/4in (8.65cm) by 5-1/2in (14cm). They came packaged as a complete set in a box or eight cards in a shrink-wrapped plastic package.

The third set of trading cards consisted of five very detailed color illustrations. These cards came in a translucent shrink-wrapped plastic package and are copyrighted, Mattel, Inc. 1982.

BARBIE™ Trading Cards c.1990 Mattel, Inc.; consisted of 300 trading cards. They came packaged in random packs of ten with a poster sold separately. Later in the year Mattel, Inc. released a deluxe set with carrying case and 320 cards (complete set plus twenty cards which were exclusive to the set). These trading cards were a flop because experienced collectors did not like the inaccurate information and descriptions on the backs of the trading cards pertaining to photo-art on the front.

The fifth trading card set was not a success either. *BARBIE™ Trading Cards* c. 1990 Mattel, Inc. consisted of 300 cards which came in random packs of ten with puzzle pieces.

Whether the weather is rain, snow, or sun – every day, every one can have BARBIE® doll fun activities.

255

255. The Dynamic Toy Company *BARBIE™ and Ken™ Jumbo Trading Cards* c. 1962.

256

257

258

256. *BARBIE® and Ken™ Jigsaw Puzzle* c. 1963 by
   Whitman® Publishing Company. Hard to find.
257. The coloring book drawings have reflected the times
   and themes, as these groovy editions of the early
   1970's represent.
258. The first coloring book was the *BARBIE® and Ken™*
   Coloring Book c. 1962, published by Western
   Publishing Company, Inc. a division of Whitman®.
   Hard to find.

259

260

261

259. ColorForms *BARBIE®*
Color and Play c. 1974.
260. Mattel, Inc. c. 1982 –
Trading Cards.
261. *Growing-Up Skipper®*
c. 1978 is a Whitman®
Publishing Company
coloring and paper
doll book.
262. The 1982 BARBIE® doll
series of six Whitman®
Publishing Company
jigsaw puzzles.

262

OPPOSITE PAGE:
263. Western Publishing
Company, Inc. has
produced Frame-Tray-
Puzzles in assorted sizes
and themes.
264. Golden® began publishing
coloring books in 1980.
265. This large *BARBIE™*
Coloring Book measures
15-1/2in (39cm) x
20in (51cm), by
Merrigold Press c. 1984.
266. Golden® began making
BARBIE® Crayons
during the 1980's.
267. Several companies have
produced sticker decals
since the 1980s.

263

264

265

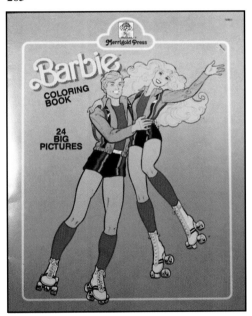

266

267

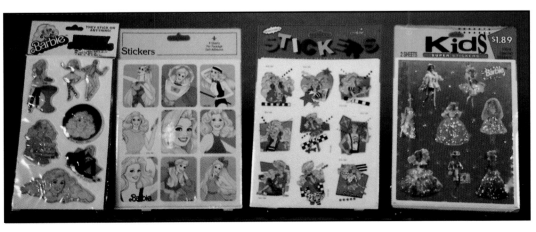

268

269

270

271

272

268. **BARBIE™ 1986 Sticker Calendar** c. 1985 by Hoyle Products – hard to find.
269. Golden® **BARBIE™ Trace & Color** books have been available in assorted themes.
270. Golden® **BARBIE™ Paint 'N' Marker Books** have been available in assorted themes.
271. **BARBIE® Diary** (1989) Webway Incorporated.
272. Golden® – Sticker Fun books have been produced in assorted themes. The **BARBIE™ and The Sensations Sticker Fun** c. 1988 book was not widely distributed.

273

274

275

276

273. **Fun Book** c. 1993 by Golden®, measures 4in (10cm) x 5-1/2in (14cm).

274. Golden® has continued the tradition of BARBIE® doll and Ken® doll in coloring books.

275. **BARBIE™ Trading Cards** c. 1990 is the fifth trading card set.

276. **BARBIE™ Trading Cards** c. 1990 Mattel, Inc. Left to right is the deluxe set, store display carton with in individually random pack package, and poster.

277. **Nostalgic BARBIE™ 550 Piece Interlocking 18in (46cm) x 24in (61cm) Jigsaw Puzzle,** 1989 by American Publishing.

277

278

279

280

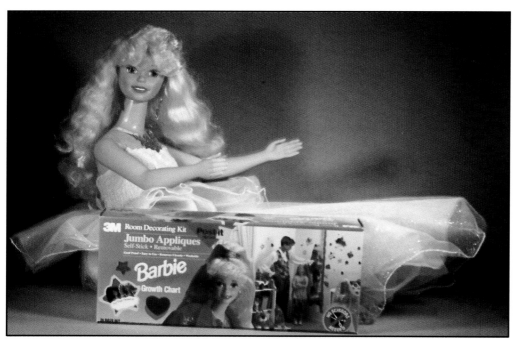

278. ***BARBIE*™ *Memories scrapbook*** c. 1991 made by Antioch Publishing Company.
279. ***BARBIE*® *Fashion Color & Play*** c. 1991, Craft House.
280. ***BARBIE*™ *for Girls*™ *Growth Chart*** c. 1993, a 3 M Room Decorating Kit. The *My Size BARBIE*® *doll* is the 38in (97cm) test market edition.

281

282

283

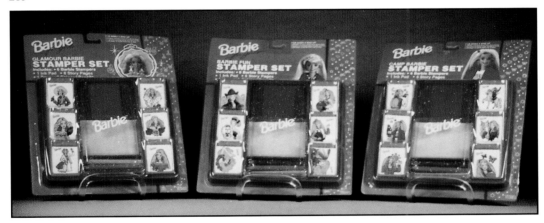

284

281. *BARBIE – Glitter Star 110 Camera*
282. *BARBIE for Girls! Fun Camera Outdoor 35 MM camera and film in one* c. 1994 by Kalimar, Inc.
283. *BARBIE for Girls Stamper Sets* c. 1994 by Tara Toy Corporation.
284. *BARBIE Notes to Color & Send* c. 1992 by Golden .

Chapter 15

DINING WITH BARBIE® DOLL

Dining with BARBIE® doll can be literal or figurative depending on a wide range of merchandise. Everything from tea services, cooking, play-act accessories, and eating a McDonald®'s "Happy Meal™".

Every little girl loves to have tea parties. The first under license tea services and dishes were made by Worchester Toy Company. They were available from store Christmas 'Wish Book' catalogs in 1961. Montgomery Ward's *Complete BARBIE™ Plastic Tea Set* a 56 piece set for six persons. The Sears® and Roebuck Company was selling *BARBIE™'s Own Tea Set* a 42 piece set for four persons. In 1962, Irwin Corporation was producing under license the *BARBIE™ Heirloom Service Playset* available from Montgomery Ward. Sears® and Roebuck Company was selling *BARBIE™ Cutlery Set*.

Tea services, dishes, and cookware are currently being made under license by Jesco, Inc./Chilton-Globe.

One can learn to cook with *The BARBIE™ Party Cookbook*, under license by Mattel, Inc. and published and copyrighted in 1991 by Price Stern Sloan, Inc.

If you wish to bake a BARBIE™ doll birthday cake, you can use the 1988 and 1992 under license BARBIE™ doll cake pan by Wilton Enterprises.

Nasta Industries in 1980, produced *BARBIE™ Ice Pops*, an ice pop mold to make three ice pops in the shape of BARBIE™ doll's head.

Through the years BARBIE® doll has had *Fun at McDonald®'s* and a *Happy Meal™* (McDonald®'s and Happy Meal are trademarks of the McDonald®'s Corporation).

Mattel, Inc. manufactured a McDonald®'s restaurant called *BARBIE™ Loves McDonald®'s Restaurant* which was available from 1983 to 1984. In 1983, there were McDonald®'s uniforms for BARBIE™ doll, Ken™ doll, and Skipper™ doll, called *BARBIE™ Fun At McDonald®'s, Ken™ Fun At McDonald®'s,* and *Skipper™ Fun At McDonald®'s.*

In 1990, selected U.S. cities were test market sites for a new Happy Meal™ BARBIE™ doll figurine premiums. It was a success. If you entered one of McDonald®'s 9,000 restaurants in August, 1991 you saw two in-store promotions or perhaps you saw a promotion when you were at the drive-thru for the $1.99 Happy Meal™ program. There was a translite and a display case inside. Outside at the drive-thru menu board was another translite. There were eight BARBIE™ doll figurines (two offered each week) in 1991 and consecutive years through 1995 (thus far). The figurines came with boxes in 1991 to 1992 and paper sacks in 1993 to 1995.

Pizza Party! Skipper® Pizza Shop c. 1994 is a Pizza Hut, Inc.® (registered trademark of PepsiCo., Inc.) restaurant and was manufactured by Mattel, Inc. as the under license party.

If "Dining with BARBIE™ Doll" should make you hungry – *Bon Appetite.*

285.

285. *Genuine BARBIE® Party Sets* have been made by Jesco, Inc./ Chilton-Globe. 31-Piece Decorated Cook 'N' Serve Set c. 1983 and 26-Piece Plastic Tea Set c. 1983.

286

287

288

286. The *BARBIE™ Loves McDonald®'s Restaurant* (1983 to 1984) hard to find. BARBIE® doll, Ken® doll, and Skipper® doll, are wearing their *Fun At McDonald®'s* uniforms, hard to find.

287. An Early advertisement for BARBIE® doll, family, and friends Thermos Brand Lunch Kits made by King-Seeley Thermos Company. Skooter® doll is wearing *School Girl* (a Skipper® fashion) and carrying a Kitty Cucumber-Sanrio mini tin lunch box, c. 1976.

288. The 1991, *McDonald®'s Happy Meal™ Display Case with BARBIE® figurines and Mattel, Inc. HOT WHEELS®* There are less than 9,000 in existence. Rare.

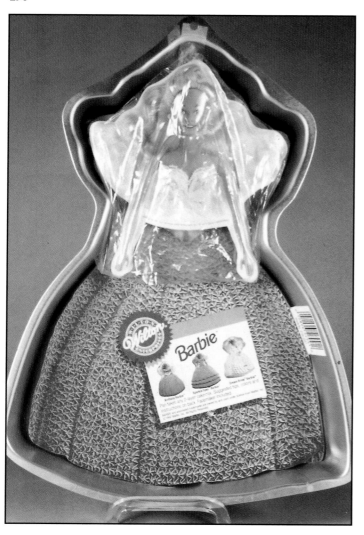

289. *BARBIE*™ *Loves McDonald*®*'s Restaurant* never removed from box – hard to find and *BARBIE*™ *Fun At McDonald*®*'s* hard to find.
290. The Wilton Enterprises produced a *BARBIE*™ *doll cake pan* c. 1992.
291. In 1989, Ralston Purina Company made *Breakfast with BARBIE*™ *Cereal.*

292

293

294

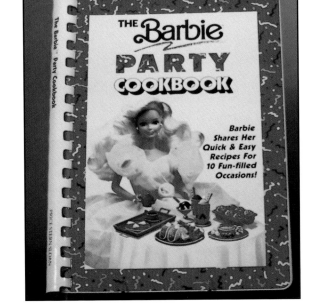

292. There were two McDonald®'s translites in 1991; are identical except for their size. The drive-thru translite is 13-3/4in (35cm) x 13-3/4in (35cm) and the instore translite is 21-1/4in (54cm) x 21-3/4in (55cm) – each are rare.

293. The 1992, *McDonald®'s Happy Meal™ Complete Display* – hard to find.

294. *The BARBIE™ Party Cookbook* c. 1990, published by Price Stern Sloan.

295

296

297

299

298

295. The 1993, **McDonald®'s Happy Meal™ Complete Display** – hard to find.

296. The 1994, **McDonald®'s Happy Meal™ Complete Display** – hard to find.

297. In 1994, McDonald®'s had a BARBIE™ doll design tray liner and test marketed the African American **Locket Surprise BARBIE™ doll figurine** and **Locket Surprise Ken™ doll figurine.**

298. **1993 McDonld®'s translite** promoting the "Happy Meal" BARBIE® doll figurine with styleable hair. Hard to find.

299. **Pizza Party! Skipper®'s Pizza Ship** c. 1994 is a Pizza Hut, Inc.® restaurant.

300

301

302

303

300. These 1995 bisque items add seasoning to one's collection! The ***BARBIE*™ & Ken*™ *Chefs Salt and Pepper Shakers*** were made under license by Enseco® Corporation.

301. Little Debbie Snack Cakes offered an exclusive, *Little Debbie BARBIE® doll* 1993.

302. The difficult to find figurine is a cake decoration marked c. 1994 Mattel, Inc., license the Enesco® Corp. It was copyrighted in 1994 by Bakery Crafts and distributed in 1995 to Kroger - The Pastery Shoppe. It was simply referred to as BARBIE® #CK-165C. This figurine is representing the #983 *Enchanted Evening* 1960 BARBIE® doll fashion.

303. The 1995 "McDonald®'s Happy Meal®" display.

304. Skipper® doll can have a pizza party with her friends Kevin® doll and Courtney® doll.

304

Chapter 16

TOUCHES OF BARBIE™ DOLL GLAMOUR

The BARBIE® doll is known for being glamorous. During the years there have been items made for BARBIE™ doll, children, and collectors with added glamour. A part of the glamour is the ability to accessorize and dramatize.

Elgin National Watch Company's subsidiary, Bradley Time Division was under license from Mattel, Inc. to manufacture BARBIE® doll character watches from 1963 to 1974. These watches were a one-jewel pin lever movement. Quite a few are still ticking to this day. Those that are not working have either one of two problems: one, the watch could be dirty or two, the pivot on the balance staff is broken. One should consult their jeweler to see if they can repair these because the company is out-of-business, thus, parts are no longer available.

A Touch of Jeweled Glamour for Every BARBIE™ Fan was the motto of Cleinman and Sons. They were

under license from Mattel, Inc. in 1962 and 1963 to make BARBIE® doll and Midge® doll jewelry.

Numerous companies through the years have made under license various hygiene products. They have been the following:

The Roclar Company circa 1960, marketed a *BARBIE® Beauty Kit* in a vinyl case which contained bubble bath and soap.

Circa 1963. Helene Curtis' slogan for their *BARBIE® Bubble Bath* was, "The Prettiest Bubbles to tickle your nose and make you feel pretty right down to your toes". They also made *BARBIE™ Shampoo.*

Merry Manufacturing Company in 1963 to 1964 sold *BARBIE® Make Believe Rouge and Powders and BARBIE® Glamour Cosmetics.*

In 1986, DuCair Bioessence began their distribution of a complete line of glamour products.

Mattel, Inc. manufactured a *BARBIE™ Perfume Maker* in 1979. This perfume chemistry-set was for the child to concoct various fragrances.

BARBIE™ doll's 30th anniversary was in 1989. Peter Brams Designs was under license to market solid sterling silver *Nostalgic BARBIE™ Charm Bracelet(s).* These were not widely distributed. In the same design were 18 karat gold plate which were easier to find in some locations.

The 35th anniversary of BARBIE® doll was in 1994. Fashion designer Nicole Miller was under license to design various adult-size apparel such as scarfs, neckties, and etc. the "Fossil" watch company introduced a line of collectible adult-size BARBIE™ doll inspired limited edition watches.

The touches of BARBIE™ doll glamour products can add pizzazz to one's BARBIE® doll collecting.

305. *SuperStar BARBIE™ Fur & Jewels Safe* (1979).

306

308

306. Bradley Time Division manufactured *BARBIE® doll character watches* from 1963 to 1974.

307. DuCair Bioessence began distribution of a complete line of glamour products in 1986. the *BARBIE™ Cologne with a Pink Bear* c. 1989 is hard to find. The wash cloth was designed by Cannon c. 1992.

308. *Nostalgic BARBIE™ Ceramic Pin*, (1989), under license by ClayArt.

309. *BARBIE®'s Wig Wardrobe* (1964) – Wigs became a glamorous fashion statement during the 1960s.

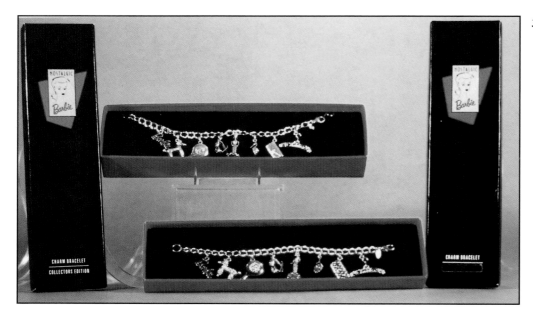

310

311

312

313

310. The Peter Brams Designs,
     ***Nostalgic BARBIE*™ *Charm
     Bracelet(s)*** were limited
     editions for BARBIE® doll's
     30th Anniversary in 1989.
     They were available in
     sterling silver and 18 Karat
     Gold Plate – hard to find.
311. ***BARBIE*™ *Musical Jewelry
     Box*** (1990) made by
     Mattel, Inc.
312. ***Perfume Pretty BARBIE®
     Gift for Two*** (1988).
313. The ***BARBIE® For Girls*™**
     was comprised of hair bows,
     bandages, cosmetics, book
     bags, etc. (1990).

315

316

314. Hope Industries designed
*BARBIE® For Girls™
character watches* in the
1990's.
315. *FAO Schwarz – BARBIE™
On Madison* exclusive
watch, 1992.
316. *Donna Karan New York
BARBIE® doll,* came in the
designer's chic fashions and
were available in brunette
hair or blonde hair.
They were exclu-
sively available at
Bloomingdale's in
1995. Each doll
carries her 'big
brown bag' (a
Bloomingdale's
shopping bag).
317. Mattel, Inc. has
produced through
the years various
enlarged BARBIE®
doll heads to
practice glamour
techniques.

314

317

320

318. ***Masquerade Ball™ BARBIE® doll,*** the sixth in the series by costume designer, Bob Mackie, is pictured with his scent, ***Mackie Perfume.*** A few dolls came with the .17 fl. oz. of ***Mackie Perfume*** – hard to find.

319. The 1995 nostalgic BARBIE® theme was ***Solo In The Spotlight*** based on the #982 BARBIE® doll fashion from 1960. Mattel, Inc. reproduced this famous fashion in 1995 available on a hard to find brunette BARBIE® doll and an easy to locate blonde. Fossil produced two watches each called "Solo In The Spotlight" boxed in grand pianos. The watch on the left in the black grand piano is sterling silver and is a limited edition of 1,000 pieces. It retailed for $180.00. An immediate rare item! The watch on the right came in pink grand piano and is limited to 20,000 pieces. It retailed for $80.00.

320. Fashion designer, Nicole Miller created a Nostalgic BARBIE™ Scarf in 1994. The Bloomingdale's 1994 exclusive ***Savvy Shopper BARBIE™ doll*** was designed by Nicole Miller.

321

322

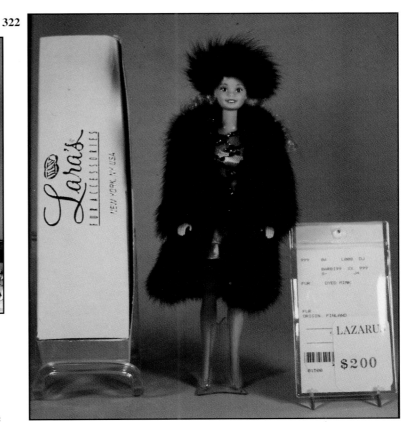

321. In 1995, the world's most famous toy store, FAO Schwarz celebrated their 125th Anniversary. To mark the event Mattel, Inc., created "Jeweled Splender BARBIE® doll" a first in a series entitled *F.A.O. Schwarz Signature Collection*. BARBIE® doll has platinum hair and wears accents of the store colors (teal, red, purple, and yellow) in her costume. The pink mirrored compact is a F.A.O. Schwarz BARBIE® doll product exclusive with their name in the bottom right hand corner and was made by Designs From The Deep, Inc.

322. Evans Furs designed for distribution in Lazarus Department Stores a BARBIE® doll size mink coat. It came in a Lara's Fur Accessories box with the BARBIE® doll, and the suggested retail price was $200.00

323

323. *BARBIE® For Girls Jewelry Box* (c. 1992) by Tara Toy Corporation.

324

324. The 1994 BARBIE® doll themed *Fossil watches* became instant collectibles. Left to Right: *35th Anniversary Accessory Watch, Pretty and Pink*, and *Charming BARBIE®* each was limited to 20,000.

Chapter 17

CALENDARS, BIRTHDAYS AND HOLIDAYS

The pages have leaped off the calendar bringing BARBIE® doll collecting to year round pursuit.

"Happy Birthday" wishes have been expressed by the under license companies. The American Greetings Corporation designed a variety of BARBIE® doll greeting cards, circa 1963. Hallmark Cards, Inc. had a BARBIE® doll birthday line in the 1980's. In 1989, Gibson Greetings, Inc. began their BARBIE® doll line. Hallmark Cards, Inc. had two nostalgic lines in 1994.

Birthday ensembles (a birthday party design with the related plates, cups, napkins, centerpiece, party favors, etc.) have been made under license. *BARBIE™ Goes To A Party* birthday ensemble was in 1965, designed by House of Paper. Hallmark Cards, Inc. had a line in 1983 called *Happy Birthday from BARBIE™!*. In 1989, (copyrighted 1985 and 1988 on packages) Unique Industries, Inc. introduced their BARBIE™ birthday ensembles. C. A. Reed (a division of the James River Company) began a 30 itemed line in 1991 which is updated to stay current and still available. Hallmark Cards, Inc. debuted their line in July, 1994 at "The Magic of BARBIE® in Birmingham" (National BARBIE™ Doll Collectors Convention), it was called, *Another Birthday BARBIE™ and Still a Doll=* (in reference to BARBIE® doll's 35th anniversary). This birthday ensemble uses photo-art of a 1959 BARBIE™ doll. It did not stay on the shelves very long.

Gift wrap had been made under license in cute designs. Flourish Gift Wrap manufactured for C.D.S. Sales, Inc. two designs circa 1980. Gibson Greetings, Inc. in 1989 had imaginative wrapping paper design to feature a BARBIE® paper doll and fashions called, *BARBIE™ doll Cut-Outs and Cut-Outs of Authentic BARBIE™ doll Fashions*. It came as a single sheet package and gift wrapping rolls. The retailers were allotted six each of either items which caused them to be hard to find in some locations. Cleo, Inc., a Gibson Greetings, Inc. company made BARBIE™ gift wrapping roll in 1992.

Easter Unlimited was under license with their c. 1983 *BARBIE™ Wrap-An Egg...Egg Decorating Kit*.

Halloween costumes have been under license since 1963 to Ben Cooper Originals throughout the 1980's. Circa 1964, at which time they were made by Collegeville Flag and Manufacturing Company.

Hallmark Cards, Inc. has created under license from Mattel, Inc. a series of three BARBIE® Keepsake Ornaments. They have created a frenzy! The series, ornaments in each series and introduction dates are as follows:

Holiday BARBIE®
 #1 1993
 #2 1994
 #3 1995

Nostalgic Series
 Debut 1959 BARBIE® 1994
 Solo In The Spotlight 1995

Springtime BARBIE™
 #1 1995
 Note: The first ornament not to have a coordinating doll.

In 1995, Mattel, Inc. issued twelve *BARBIE™ Fashion Greeting Cards* and they too were selling out. Nostalgic calendars have been popular under license since 1989.

Throughout the calendar year BARBIE® doll collectibles can be added to one's collection.

325

326

327

328

325. Flourish Gift Wrap manufactured for C.D.S. Sales, Inc. had two designs, circa 1980.
326. *BARBIE™ doll Cut-Outs and Cut-Outs of Authentic BARBIE™ doll Fashions* designed by Gibson Greetings, Inc. (1989) – hard to find.
327. Hallmark Cards, Inc. – *Happy Birthday from BARBIE™!* birthday plates c. 1983.
328. *BARBIE™ Wrap-An-Egg...Decorating Kit* c. 1983 was made by Easter Unlimited – rare.

329

330

329. Gibson Greetings, Inc. greeting cards have BARBIE® doll paper dolls and jigsaw puzzles – hard to find.

330. Gibson Greetings, Inc. began their BARBIE® doll line of greeting cards in 1989.

331. Unique Industries, Inc. introduced their BARBIE™ doll birthday ensemble in 1989. The birthday candle is very unique.

331

332

333

334

332. Gibson Greetings,
Inc.'s division, Cleo,
has produced a line of
children's valentines.
333. *Nostalgic BARBIE*™
Calendars by Gibson
Greetings, Inc.
334. *Nostalgic BARBIE*™
Calendars by
Design Look.

335

336

337

335. The postcard books were produced by Running Press – The American Postcard Company. They were *Nostalgic BARBIE*™ c. 1990 and *Forever BARBIE*™ c. 1991.
336. The gift bags are c. 1992 and c. 1993 by Gibson Greetings, Inc.
337. The 1993 *Happy Holiday BARBIE*™ *doll* and *#1 Holiday Hallmark Keepsake Ornament* (hard to find) and Hallmark shoppe counter top display (rare).
338. Hallmark Cards, Inc. had twelve BARBIE® greeting cards in 1994.

338

339

340

341

339. *BARBIE® Party Time* c. 1992.
340. 1995 Calendar by Hallmark Cards, Inc.
341. Hallmark Cards, Inc. *Glamour Dream Collection - BARBIE™* c. 1994.

342

343

344

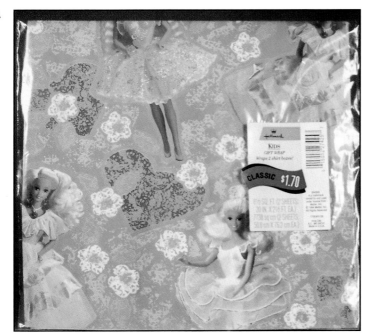

342. ***Another Birthday BARBIE™ and Still A Doll***
c. 1994 was Hallmark Cards, Inc. birthday
ensemble.

343. The ***35th Anniversary BARBIE® Keepsake
Collection*** gift set, Hallmark Keepsake
Ornament, ***Nostalgic Series – Debut 1959
BARBIE®*** and Hallmark store display
promotional sign – hard to find.

344. 1994 Hallmark Cards, Inc. wrapping paper.

345

346

347

348

345. ***BARBIE® Fashion Greeting Card*** – "Happy Holidays" was a new line in 1995 with various festive dresses.

346. 1994 Hallmark Cards, Inc. wrapping paper and gift card.

347. C. A. Reed and McDonald®'s Restaurants began in 1994 children's birthday parties. There was a fifteen car birthday train Happy Meal™ promotions with a special ***Happy Birthday Special Guest BARBIE®*** train piece. However this piece was recalled due to breakage exposing a metal rod. Also shown is the McDonald®'s toy reference card.

348. The 1994 ***Happy Holiday BARBIE™ doll***, Hallmark Keepsake Ornament, ***Holiday BARBIE® #2*** and Hallmark display.

349

350

351

352

349. The Hallmark Keepsake Ornament 1995, *Springtime BARBIE™ - #1*.

350. *BARBIE™ Fashion Greeting Cards* c. 1995, Mattel, Inc.

351. *Hallmark BARBIE™ Valentines* (1995) is a box of thirty children's Valentines.

352. A 1995 line of greeting cards by Ambassador Cards (division of Hallmark Cards, Inc.) featured various BARBIE™ dolls. The card shown depicts *The Great Eras Collection – Volume Four – 1850's Southern Belle BARBIE® doll*.

353

354

355

353. Hallmark *Glamour Dream Collection – BARBIE™ Greeting Cards* (1995).

354. Third in the *Hallmark Keepsake Ornament – Holiday BARBIE™ Series* was available in 1995.

355. Second in the *Hallmark Keepsake BARBIE™ Doll Ornament*. Series was "Solo in the Spotlight BARBIE™" 1995.

356. Inspired by antique greeting cards and were exclusively available at Hallmark – Gold Crown Stores are *Victorian Elegance BARBIE™ doll* first in the series (1994) and *Holiday Memories BARBIE™ doll* second in the series (1995).

356

Chapter 18

MATTEL, INC.'S
PROMOTIONS AND PREMIUMS

1995 was a landmark year for Mattel, Inc. because it marked their 50th anniversary. Harold Matson and Elliot Handler coined the company name by combining the nickname of Matson – which was Matt – with the first two letters of Elliot, when combined, forms "Mattel".

Mattel began in 1945, in the southern California garage of Harold Matson. Elliot Handler and Harold Matson designed and produced from scrap plastic and wood picture frames and dollhouse furniture. The company quickly out-grew the garage and moved to a 60,000 square-foot factory in Los Angeles, California.

The Mattel Toy Company moved its headquarters to Hawthorne, California in December 1959. In the mid-1970's Mattel, Inc. had a major change in leadership and since that time have had various company presidents and board of directors. The decision was made to move the world headquarters to El Segundo, California and they have been located there since 1991.

The ad agency, Carson/Roberts was hired by Mattel, Inc. in 1955 to promote their toys. An unprecedented idea (at the time) was to be a segment sponsor of the ABC (American Broadcasting Company) television network's new show produced by Walt Disney® and titled "The Mickey Mouse Club".

The early 1960's BARBIE® doll television commercials portrayed her image as a svelte fashion model.

Mattel, Inc. was the first toy company to use store displays. The store displays were to showcase to consumers the aspects of product design, function, and in-store advertising. Store displays are made in very limited numbers and are not available to the general public.

Promotions and premiums have been offered to consumers through the years. They usually are mail-in offers and available for a short period of time.

The Toy Club™ is the Mattel, Inc. employee store that has sold various toys and items not initially available elsewhere, if, at all.

Mattel, Inc. celebrates their golden 50th anniversary, with the achievement of being the world's largest toy company. Ruth and Elliot Handler paved the path with innovations and creativity for the entire toy industry.

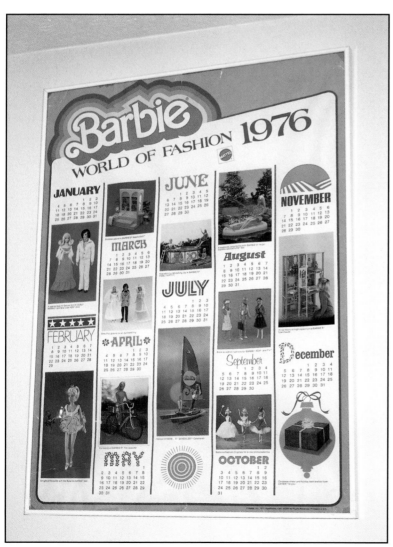

357. **1976 BARBIE® World of Fashion Calendar**, came free with purchase – Rare.

358

359

360

361

358. An advertisement promoting, *Talking BARBIE® doll and friends* appearance on Saturday, November 16, 1968 television show, "Get Smart". The episode was entitled, "The Ugliest Girl".

359. Ruth Handler created the BARBIE® doll and this very rare match book has her name in gold script. The *Montgomery Ward BARBIE® doll* (1972) is on the left.

360. Mattel, Inc. c. 1980, *BARBIE® Licensee Book.*

361. The *BARBIE® Le Nouveau Theatre De La Mode* (1985) was especially created by Billy Boy for Mattel France to commemorate 26 years of BARBIE® doll. This was a 10,000 limited edition. The one shown is signed by Billy Boy and the majority were not! The booklets are from Mattel France incollaboration with Billy Boy for his train exposition and from the United States "BARBIE® On Tour". The brunette doll is *Feelin' Groovy BARBIE® Doll* (1986) – All are rare and hard to find.

362

363

364

365

362. ***Mattel Wish List booklets.***
363. BARBIE® and The Rockers™ record, ***"In Concert"*** was available free in Los Angeles, California at "BARBIE® On Tour" (1986).
364. ***BARBIE® Fashions*** was a 1983 store display with fashion cards – very rare.
365. Mattel, Inc. store displays of the 1980s.

366

367

368

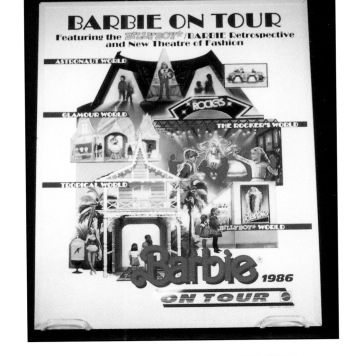

369

366. *Jewel Secret BARBIE® doll and Jewel Secret Ken® doll* was a store display in 1987 – rare.
367. 1987 Mattel, Inc. department store catalogue. These are not available to the general public.
368. *BARBIE® On Tour 1986* poster was available on the United States tour.
369. The Mattel, Inc. The Toy Club™ is the employee store. In 1989 these exclusive *BARBIE® Fan On Board* sign for vehicle windows were available.

370

371

372

370. 1988 Mattel, Inc. company catalogue and Collectors Classics catalogue. These are not available to the general public.
371. *BARBIE™ Birthday Party at Walt Disney World® - Epcot® '94* was a 1994 1¢ VHS video promotional.
372. *Pink Jubilee BARBIE® store displays.* (1989) hard to find.
373. Two 1991 *Happy Meal™ BARBIE® doll figurines* shown with boxes – boxes are hard to find.

373

374. **BARBIE® Magazine – 35th Anniversary Issue for Retailers** c. 1994 was distributed by Mattel, Inc. It shows illustrations of various phototype items that were to be available in 1995. Rare.

375. 1989 Mattel, Inc. company catalogue and Collectors Classics catalogue. These are not available to the general public.

376. **Summit BARBIE® doll** store display for the 1990 First Annual Children's Summit.

377. *1991 Sneak Preview Calendar* came with a fashion that is on the BARBIE® on the left, (hair styled by the author). **BARBIE® 1991 line** mail order promotional book with entire line.

376

377

378

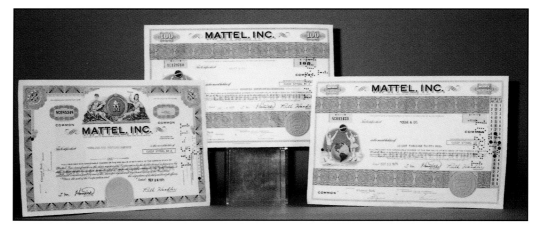

379

380

381

378. Mattel, Inc. was incorporated in 1968 and shares of stock have been available on the New York Stock Exchange. These common stock certificates have past company President, Ruth Handler's signature on each.

379. 1991 Store display pictures – hard to find.

380. A 1966 mail-in offer from Palmolive Soap for BARBIE doll's and Skipper doll's tiny sister, Tutti doll. To receive Tutti doll one had to send three soap wrappers and a check or money order for a $1.75. Rare.

381. Mattel, Inc. *The Toy Club 35th Anniversary BARBIE Pin* and *The Toy Club 35th Anniversary Brunette BARBIE doll* a limited edition of 1,500 – rare.

382

383

384

382. 1993 mail in offer from McDonald®'s Corporation and Mattel, Inc. – was a VHS video called ***BARBIE® Fashion Secrets.***

383. Mattel, Inc. ***Report To Stock Holders*** of the 1990's quarter reports and annual reports have featured BARBIE® doll one of the toy company's core brands.

384. 1994 Mattel, Inc. Timeless Creations catalogue.

Chapter 19

COMMEMORATIVE MERCHANDISE

BARBIE™ doll is the world's most renowned fashion doll with resilient longevity. She debuted on March 9th, 1959 at the New York Toy Fair.

Mattel, Inc. has publicized BARBIE® doll for years, often by celebrating the various milestones with birthdays and anniversaries. When BARBIE® doll celebrated her 25th, it was her last "birthday". From 1984 to date "birthdays" have been referred to as anniversaries. Mattel, Inc.'s reasoning behind this was not to "age" BARBIE® doll in the eyes of children and maintain youthfulness. The strategy has worked. Although, Skipper® doll has gradually been growing-up since 1975.

Pewter spoons and pewter thimbles were sold through direct purchase in 1982 by Downs' Collector Showcase. BARBIE® Bathing Suit and BARBIE® Baby Sitter spoons and thimbles were made under license by Mattel, Inc.

The "1959-1984 25th Anniversary BARBIE™ China Service" was made by Jesco, Inc./Chilton-Globe under license from Mattel, Inc. This china service was a limited edition of 25,000. There has been confusion among collectors regarding sets having its certificate of authenticity and hanging tag, and those sets not having either. The china service with certificate and hanging tag was available in doll shoppes in 1984 with a suggested retail price of $55.00. Three years later, circa 1987, discount buy-out stores were selling seconds (the glazed over decal designs on the china service are crooked) for approximately $10.00 but, they are a part of the limited edition. There is a substantial price difference on the secondary market as there should be.

Since 1984, each additional five-year anniversary is commemorated in various merchandise.

The media has always had a watchful eye on the world of BARBIE® doll and collectors have had the enjoyment of collecting. Mattel, Inc. has noticed both and made or given an 'under license' to various companies to make assorted commemorative merchandise.

385

385. *Mattel, Inc. 1994 BARBIE® 35th Anniversary BARBIE® Festival Banquet Dolls*, autographed by Jill E. Barad, President and Chief Operating Officer of Mattel, Inc. The festival tote bag, convention package, and author's name badge is located on the banquet centerpiece bow. Rare.

386.   ***30th Anniversary BARBIE® poster*** (1989) by Press One Printing.

387

388

389

387. The Silver Anniversary edition, *BARBIE*®
Through The Years is c. 1984,
Mattel, Inc. – rare.
388. The *1959-1984 25th Anniversary*™
China Service was available with
certificate and hanging tag in doll
shoppes at the time of introduction. The
service on the left is hard to find; on the
right is the "second". Notice the crooked
design on the tray.
389. A 1970 Mattel, Inc. advertisement
proclaimed, "BARBIE® is the Number 1
doll. There is no number 2..."

390

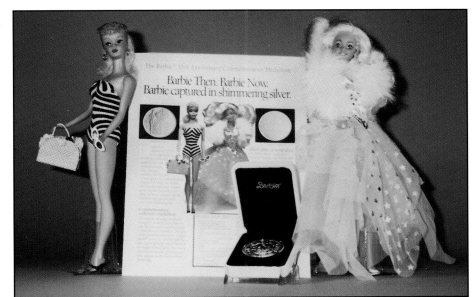

391

392

390. ***BARBIE® 30th Anniversary Commemorative Medallion*** is 1 oz. of pure silver in a pink velvet box. Not shown is the silver plated medallion, which came in a black pouch.

391. ***Mattel, Inc. 1994 BARBIE® 35th Anniversary BARBIE® Festival***. Items from the Festival Store are the official festival souvenir pin, (limited edition of 4,000), key ring, and cap.

392. The Danbury Mint has made two series of plates and figurines.

393

394

395

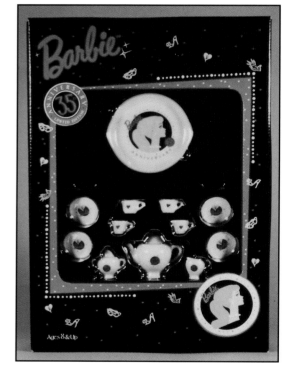

396

393. ***Dream Doll, The Ruth Handler Story*** and the *elusive Gold Jubilee BARBIE™ doll*, (limited edition: 5,000 in the United States, 2,000 for International distribution, and 200 for Mattel employees).

394. ***Mattel, Inc. 1994 BARBIE® 35th Anniversary BARBIE® Festival.*** Items from the limited edition sale collection are: 35th Anniversary Festival BARBIE®, Nostalgic 35th Anniversary Gift Set, signed by Ruth Handler, and signed Ruth Handler and Elliot Handler 1962 photograph. Rare.

395. ***BARBIE® 35th Anniversary China Service*** c. 1994. Chilton-Globe.

396. ***Christian Dior BARBIE® doll*** (1995) is a vinyl interpretation that was first unveiled in December 1993 as a wax model of BARBIE® doll that is on display in the Musee Grevin in Paris, France.

Chapter 20

GLOBAL DOLLS AND ACCESSORIES

Throughout the span of BARBIE® doll's longevity, dolls and accessories have been sold around the globe. Mattel, Inc. has been an international toy company since the early 1960's and continues to expand their global market.

The BARBIE® doll is the world's best selling doll – 800 million dolls have been sold around the world since 1959. In 1968, Mattel, Inc. was selling in over 60 countries and 27 years later (1995) it is selling in 140 nations. Two dolls are sold somewhere in the world every second.

The BARBIE® doll and accessories have represented the cultures of the country where they have been sold. These items are elusive to the United States; in some instances and hard to obtain for the people who live in other countries.

Whereas some items have been exactly the same or similar, other things have been very different. In some parts of the world the marketing is under license. In other corners of the globe, Mattel, Inc. produces BARBIE® doll and accessories. Regardless of the language, BARBIE® doll is a recognizable symbol throughout the world.

The European market has had some very unique accessories. In Japan (as well as other nations) their version(s) of the BARBIE® doll, were their vision of *Americans*.

Global dolls and accessories is a fascinating aspect to the world of BARBIE® doll collecting.

397

397. **BARBIE® Dream Carriage** was also available in Europe and Canada, 1982.

398

399

400

401

398. *Patio furniture* from Germany c. 1977 is perfect for an old fashioned American Independence Day.

399. The German *Freundschafts (Friendship) BARBIE® doll* c. 1990 was to commemorate the tearing down of the Berlin Wall and the reunification of Germany. She is the first BARBIE® doll to be sold in eastern and central European nations.

400. The European, *BARBIE® Dream Carriage* was available with three changeable door panels in 1982. Hard to find.

401. The *Takara BARBIE® doll and Ken® doll* were available exclusively in Japan.

402. *Journal BARBIE*® are *German BARBIE*® *Fan Club publications.*
403. The mini copy, *Vogue-France* magazine was a Mattel France promotional.
The miniature supplement was inserted in the March 1988 issue of *Vogue-France*.

404

405

404. *BARBIE® Winter Garden* 1987 from Italy. Rare.

405. *BARBIE® trading cards* from Canada were made by, Action-Banini, 1991 and 1992.

406. **BARBIE**® **Winter Garden** is capable of being a real greenhouse.

407

408

409

407. **BARBIE® Hundesede (dog sled)** c. 1981, available in Scandinavian nations. Very, very, rare.

408. From Brazil is **BARBIE® Feliz Aniversario (Happy Birthday)** doll was made by Estrela Brinquedos. Rare.

409. 1988 Calgary Olympic Winter games. **Skating Star BARBIE® doll**, is from Canada.

410. Korean BARBIE® dolls are *Dancing Cinderella BARBIE® doll* and *BARBIE® doll*.
411. *Champion BARBIE® doll Horse*, 1991 from Italy.

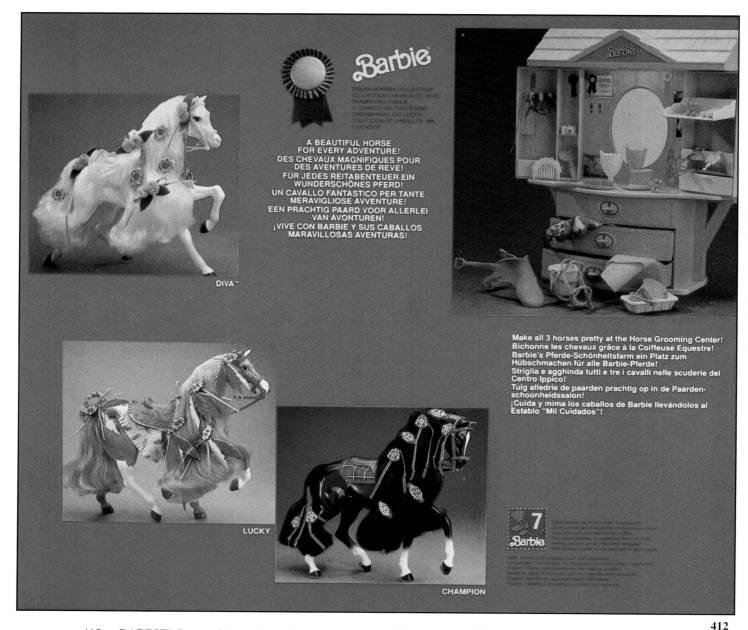

412. ***BARBIE® Dream Horse Collection, Diva, Lucky, Champion and The Horse Grooming Center.***
These were available in Italy (1991).

EPILOGUE

The world of BARBIE® doll is a quest and adventure. There are discoveries still being made in various places from doll shows to the BARBIE® doll isle in toy stores.

Since, I am an "everything" BARBIE® doll collector, my goal has been to share my enthusiasm and to apprise the collector. There is a wide spectrum of accessories to collect. BARBIE® doll collectors have extensive alternatives. Three decades and counting have amassed a gigantic list of collectibles and regardless of its era, one can have a vast or specialty interest.

It is evident that collections require space and money (paper money or plastic does not grow on trees). BARBIE® doll collecting is very fervent around the globe.

This book has been an endeavor to cultivate the novice and advance the collector. Furthermore, to shed a light on the *Treasury of BARBIE® Doll Accessories.*

TIPS ON BARBIE® COLLECTING

1. Choose a speciality interest in the realm of BARBIE® doll collecting.

2. The correct era dolls in their appropriate fashions should be displayed with accessories.

3. Educate yourself to be a knowledgeable collector, the BARBIE® doll world is full of discoveries.

4. To clean vinyl or plastic use mild soap and water. If you use something strong, test in an inconspicuous spot first.

5. Take pleasure in your collection.

ABOUT THE AUTHOR

Rebecca Ann Rupp has actively been involved with BARBIE® dolls and accessories since she received her first BARBIE® doll at the age of four. She is not only an avid collector of BARBIE® dolls and accessories but is also a modern collector of toys and dolls.

Rebecca has shared her BARBIE® expertise through club membership, slide presentations, programs, seminars, workshops at conventions and through various news interviews. An immediate past officer and member of the U.F.D.C. Derby City Doll Club of Kentucky, Rebecca designed the club's logo. In 1988, Derby City Doll Club hosted their Region 8 Conference, "Vive Les Bébés" at which time they sponsored Rebecca's first exhibit, "Welcome to BARBIE®town U.S.A."; the appellation she gave her collection at the age of nine. The convention report in *Doll Castle News* magazine included this popular exhibit. In addition, Rebecca served as chairperson of the "Fashionable BARBIE® Doll Luncheon". She was editorial asssistant and staff writer for "Vive Les Bébés" souvenir book, as well as contributing writer of articles published by various other doll publications.

"Around The World With The International BARBIE® Dolls" was a well received seminar and slide program she presented at the "BARBIE® Loves A Fairy Tale" National BARBIE® Doll Convention.

Nationally known as a dealer and appraiser of modern collectible dolls, Rebecca has served in the competition room at the National BARBIE® Doll Convention and is on her way to becoming a judge. Print and television media have interviewed her on various BARBIE® topics. The *Scene Magazine*, supplement to *The Courier-Journal*, Lousiville, KY, interviewed her in regards to BARBIE® doll's 30th Anniversary. Rebecca has also been interviewed by ABC and CBS affiliates in regards to her collection and exhibits. She has appeared on the following programs: "Bernson's Corner", "PM Magazine", "Breakfast With BARBIE®" on "Good Morning Kentuckiana" and "American Journal".

Rebecca Ann Rupp is truly a first generation BARBIE® doll player. Collecting BARBIE® dolls and accessories has been her lifelong hobby and career.

Chapter 1 – PAPER DOLL HISTORY AND CHRONOLOGY

Item	Price	I Have	I Want
BARBIE® and Ken®	$ 90	☐	☐
BARBIE® Doll Cut-Outs	70	☐	☐
BARBIE®, Ken® and Midge®	75	☐	☐
Midge®, BARBIE®'s Best Friend Cut-Outs	70	☐	☐
BARBIE® Costume Dolls	115	☐	☐
BARBIE® and Skipper®	70	☐	☐
BARBIE®, Midge®, and Skipper®	50	☐	☐
Skipper® and Skooter™ Four Season Wardrobe	45	☐	☐
Skipper® , BARBIE®'s Little Sister	70	☐	☐
Skooter®, Skipper®'s Best Friend	50	☐	☐
BARBIE®, Skipper®, Skooter®	50	☐	☐
Meet Francie®, BARBIE®'s Modern Cousin and Casey	40	☐	☐
BARBIE® and Francie®, BARBIE®'s Modern Cousin	30	☐	☐
BARBIE® has a new look!	55	☐	☐
Tutti®	30	☐	☐
BARBIE®, Christie and Stacey BARBIE®'s New Friend	45	☐	☐
New 'N Groovy P.J.	25	☐	☐
Malibu BARBIE®/The Sun Set	18	☐	☐
BARBIE®'s Boutique	45	☐	☐
BARBIE®'s Friendship	35	☐	☐
Francie® with Grow 'N Pretty Hair	25	☐	☐
Malibu Francie®	18	☐	☐
Malibu Skipper®	18	☐	☐
Yellowstone Kelley	25	☐	☐

Item	Price	I Have	I Want
BARBIE®'s Fashion Original	16	☐	☐
SuperStar BARBIE®	15	☐	☐
Fashion Photo BARBIE® and P.J	25	☐	☐
BARBIE®'s design-a-fashion paper doll kit	15	☐	☐
BARBIE® and Skipper®/Campsite at Lucky Lake	12	☐	☐
Western BARBIE®	15	☐	☐
Pink and Pretty BARBIE®/Paper Doll Playbook	15	☐	☐
Pink and Pretty BARBIE®	12	☐	☐
(Angel Face) BARBIE® Paper Doll Boxed Set	15	☐	☐
Crystal BARBIE® Paper Doll Boxed Set	12	☐	☐
BARBIE® and Ken®	12	☐	☐
Day-to-Night BARBIE®	15	☐	☐
BARBIE® and The Rockers®	15	☐	☐
Jewel Secrets BARBIE®	12	☐	☐
SuperStar BARBIE® (illustrated cover)	12	☐	☐
SuperStar BARBIE® (photo art cover)	8	☐	☐
Peck-Grande™ Presents – Nostalgic Series	20 each	☐	☐
BARBIE® and The Beat On Tour/Playset	17	☐	☐
Golden Miniature – BARBIE® Paper Doll Cut-Outs	8	☐	☐
BARBIE® – 2nd Logo	10	☐	☐
BARBIE® – 3rd Logo	5	☐	☐
BARBIE® Golden Deluxe (More Fashions)	5	☐	☐
BARBIE® Golden Boxed Set	10	☐	☐
BARBIE®, 1993	5	☐	☐
BARBIE®, 1994	10	☐	☐
Peck Aubry Nostalgic Collection	10 each	☐	☐
Golden Boxed Sets	5 each	☐	☐

Chapter 2 – TRAVELING WITH BARBIE® DOLL

Item	Price	I Have	I Want
Ponytail c	$20	☐	☐
Ken®	40	☐	☐
BARBIE® and Midge®	50	☐	☐
Skipper®	25	☐	☐
Skipper® and Skooter™	45	☐	☐
BARBIE® Trousseau	140	☐	☐
BARBIE® and Ken® Costume Trunk	175	☐	☐
Fashion Queen	95	☐	☐
Miss BARBIE®	125	☐	☐
BARBIE® and Skipper® Travel Trunk "Picnic"	140	☐	☐
BARBIE®, Francie®, and Skipper® Trunk	125	☐	☐

Item	Price	I Have	I Want
Francie® "Six-Sided"	45	☐	☐
Tutti® Playhouse	140	☐	☐
Tutti®	25	☐	☐
The World of BARBIE® Doll Case	20	☐	☐
The World of BARBIE® Doll Trunk	30	☐	☐
BARBIE® Mountain Ski Cabin	40	☐	☐
BARBIE® and Steffie Sleep 'N Keep Case	75	☐	☐
Sleep 'N Keep Case	35	☐	☐
BARBIE® On Madison – FAO Schwarz exclusive	30	☐	☐
BARBIE® Hangers	12	☐	☐
Doll Scale Four-piece Luggage Set	25	☐	☐

	Price	I Have	I Want
ADI – Pencil Cases	5	☐	☐
BARBIE® Style Book Bag	22	☐	☐
BARBIE® Style Carry-All	12	☐	☐
Applause – Expand-A-Files	25	☐	
BARBIE® Hollywood Suitcase	12	☐	☐
BARBIE® Tons of Drawers	10	☐	☐
BARBIE™ Take-A-Long	20	☐	☐

Chapter 3 – FAN CLUBS AND PERIODICALS

	Price	I Have	I Want
Dell Comic Magazines			
May - July 1962	$195	☐	☐
August - October 1962	175	☐	☐
May - July 1963	175	☐	☐
August - October 1963	175	☐	☐
November - January 1964	245	☐	☐
New BARBIE® Fan Club Membership Kit	35	☐	☐
BARBIE® Talk Magazine	20	☐	☐
BARBIE® The Magazine for Girls			
Premier Issue	20	☐	☐
Regular Issues	8	☐	☐
Special Issues	12	☐	☐
Happy Holidays BARBIE® doll Cover Issues	15	☐	☐
Target Exclusive	18	☐	☐
BARBIE® doll 30th Anniversary Issue	16	☐	☐
BARBIE® Doll Through the Years booklet	10	☐	☐
Marvel Entertainment Comic Books			
BARBIE® – 1st Issue	10	☐	☐
BARBIE® Fashion – 1st Issue	10	☐	☐
BARBIE® – #2 through #12	7	☐	☐
BARBIE® Fashion – #2 through #12	7	☐	☐

Chapter 4 – BARBIE® DOLL STORY BOOKS

	Price	I Have	I Want
Random House Books	$40 each	☐	☐
BARBIE® Goes To A Party	30	☐	☐
BARBIE® The Baby Sitter	20	☐	☐
BARBIE® Adventures – To Read Aloud	20	☐	☐
Portrait of Skipper®	15	☐	☐
A-Tell-A-Tale			
BARBIE® and Skipper® Go Camping	5	☐	☐
BARBIE® On Skates	2	☐	☐
Golden			
My Very Own Diary By BARBIE®	15	☐	☐
BARBIE® and The Rockers – The Hottest Group In Town	10	☐	☐
BARBIE® and The Rockers – The Fan	10	☐	☐
BARBIE® A Picnic Surprise book and tape	8	☐	☐
BARBIE® The Big Splash book and tape	8	☐	☐
BARBIE® Show Time!	4	☐	☐
A Little Golden Books			
BARBIE®	15	☐	☐
The Fairy Princess SuperStar BARBIE®	12	☐	☐
The Missing Wedding Dress Featuring BARBIE®	10	☐	☐
BARBIE® A Picnic Surprise	8	☐	☐
BARBIE® The Big Splash	6	☐	☐
Very Busy BARBIE®	4	☐	☐
BARBIE® Soccer Coach	2	☐	☐
Book Marks by Antioch Publishing Company	3 each	☐	☐
Golden Sound Story			
BARBIE® The Island Resort Adventure	10	☐	☐
BARBIE® Birthday Surprise for Skipper®	10	☐	☐

Chapter 5 – BARBIE® DOLLHOUSES

	Price	I Have	I Want
1st Dream House	$195	☐	☐
New Dream House	295	☐	☐
BARBIE® Kitchen and Dinette	250	☐	☐
BARBIE® and Skipper® Deluxe Dream House	125	☐	☐
BARBIE® Family Deluxe House	200	☐	☐
Skipper® Dream Room	250	☐	☐
Francie® House	100	☐	☐
Skipper® Deluxe Dream House	250	☐	☐
BARBIE® Family House	75	☐	☐
Lively Livin' House	110	☐	☐
BARBIE® Surprise House	150	☐	☐
Country Living Home	85	☐	☐
Jamie's Penthouse	110	☐	☐
BARBIE® Townhouse	60	☐	☐
Ken® Playpack – Ken® at Work	20	☐	☐

Chapter 6 – BARBIE® DOLL HOME FURNISHINGS

	I Have	I Want		I Have	I Want
Suzy Goose Hutches			BARBIE® Beauty Bath 35	☐	☐
with drawer $75	☐	☐	BARBIE®'s Pool Party 50	☐	☐
without drawer 55	☐	☐	Dream Furniture ....20 each	☐	☐
Suzy Goose Piano 240	☐	☐	Dream House Finishing Touches ....12 each	☐	☐
Suzy Goose Vanity and Bench 100	☐	☐	BARBIE® Fashion Dining Room Set 30	☐	☐
Suzy Goose Wardrobe 95	☐	☐	BARBIE® Action Accents ....2 to 6 each	☐	☐
Suzy Goose Bed 75	☐	☐	BARBIE® Bedroom Accents 18	☐	☐
Skipper® Bunk Beds 180	☐	☐	Pink Sparkles Furniture ....15 each	☐	☐
Go-Together Furniture 65	☐	☐	American Toy and Furniture Company		
J.C. Penney® Bedroom Suite 95	☐	☐	BARBIE® Night Stand 125	☐	☐

Chapter 7 – GROOVY VIBRATIONS AND MELODIES

	I Have	I Want		I Have	I Want
BARBIE® Sings! $90	☐	☐	Ice Capades 50th Anniversary Skating Rink 75	☐	☐
SPP Record Tote 65	☐	☐	Ice Capades BARBIE® doll 65	☐	☐
The Musical World of BARBIE® records ....40 each	☐	☐	Ice Capades Ken® doll 65	☐	☐
Donny & Marie Osmond T.V. Show Playset 150	☐	☐	BARBIE® The Look 15	☐	☐
Donny Osmond doll 50	☐	☐	BARBIE® and The Beat Dance Cafe 35	☐	☐
Marie Osmond doll 50	☐	☐	BARBIE® Birthday Party at Walt Disney World –		
Jimmy Osmond doll 70	☐	☐	Epcot® '94 video 20	☐	☐
"Tomy" Musical Grand Piano 75	☐	☐	Disney® Exclusives		
Kid Stuff Record Albums			Disney® Fun BARBIE® doll 45	☐	☐
Long Playing Records ....10 each	☐	☐	Disney® Fun BARBIE® doll Two 35	☐	☐
BARBIE® and Her Friends Record 30	☐	☐	Cassette Player with Headset & Microphone 35	☐	☐
BARBIE® Electronic Piano 95	☐	☐	Enesco® Corporation		
BARBIE® and The Rockers – "In Concert" Record 18	☐	☐	1994, Promotional Booklet 5	☐	☐
BARBIE® and the Rockers Live Concert Instruments 18	☐	☐	1994, Promotional Button 5	☐	☐
Hi-Tops VHS Video Cassette Tapes ....30 each	☐	☐	Action Musical – "Let's Go To The Hop" 125	☐	☐
Sensations Jukebox Music Shop 45	☐	☐	Musical Figurines – "Glamour Collection" ....85 each	☐	☐
Sensations BARBIE® doll 80	☐	☐	FAO Schwarz Rockette BARBIE® doll 250	☐	☐
Sensations Becky doll 55	☐	☐	FAO Schwarz Rockette BARBIE® doll signed by		
Sensations Bobsy doll 45	☐	☐	the Rockettes 350	☐	☐
Sensations Belinda doll 40	☐	☐	BARBIE® Festival Autograph Card signed by designer		
Bobby BiBops doll 210	☐	☐	Ann Driskill 25	☐	☐
BARBIE® Dance Club Doll and Tape Player 85	☐	☐	BARBIE™ Solo in the Spotlight Telephone 100	☐	☐

Chapter 8 – WINNING GAMES

	I Have	I Want		I Have	I Want
The BARBIE® Game – Queen of the Prom $45	☐	☐	Shopping Spree – Giant Card Game 5	☐	☐
Keys To Fame 35	☐	☐	Hi-Tech Expressions Entertainment 35	☐	☐
BARBIE®'s Little Sister Skipper® 75	☐	☐	Travel Game 5	☐	☐
Miss Lively Livin' BARBIE® 30	☐	☐	Dream Date 10	☐	☐
BARBIE® World of Fashion 55	☐	☐	The BARBIE® Game – Queen of the Prom –		
1979, Nasta BARBIE® Playing Cards 15	☐	☐	35th Anniversary Edition 60	☐	☐
The BARBIE® Game 18	☐	☐	BARBIE® Butterfly Princess™ Game 12	☐	☐
We Girls Can Do Anything 15	☐	☐	BARBIE® Dress Up Game 10	☐	☐
BARBIE® Charms The World 30	☐	☐	POG™ Fun BARBIE® doll 15	☐	☐
Queen of the Prom – 1990's Edition 15	☐	☐			

Chapter 9 – Transportation – Wheels, Wings, and Speed Boats

Item	Price	I Have	I Want	Item	Price	I Have	I Want
BARBIE®'s Sports Car	$150	☐	☐	Ferrari	50	☐	☐
BARBIE®'s and Ken®'s Hot Rod	180	☐	☐	'57 Chevy	95	☐	☐
Corvette (Irwin)	90	☐	☐	BARBIE® Around Town Scooter	18	☐	☐
Allen's Roadster	125	☐	☐	Porsche 911 Cabriolet	50	☐	☐
Sports Plane	350	☐	☐	Ford Mustang	20	☐	☐
Irwin Speedboat	200	☐	☐	Camp BARBIE® Sun Cruiser	12	☐	☐
Country Camper	30	☐	☐	Swim 'N Dive BARBIE® Speedboat	25	☐	☐
Sun 'N Fun Buggy	35	☐	☐	Jaguar XJS	50	☐	☐
United Airlines BARBIE® Friend Ship	185	☐	☐	BARBIE® doll Expandable Ford Mustang	50	☐	☐
Ten Speeder	35	☐	☐	BARBIE® Sports Cruiser	10	☐	☐
Beach Bus	50	☐	☐	Baywatch Remote Control Rescue Cruiser	18	☐	☐
Classy Corvette	175	☐	☐	Baywatch Rescue Wheels	15	☐	☐
Star "Vette"	125	☐	☐	Baywatch Rescue Station	20	☐	☐
BARBIE® Travelin' Trailer/Off-Road Vehicle and Horse Trailer	75	☐	☐	Baywatch Rescue Boat	15	☐	☐
Ken® Dream "Vette"	110	☐	☐				

Chapter 10 – Scene Presentation

Item	Price	I Have	I Want	Item	Price	I Have	I Want
Fashion Shop	$275	☐	☐	California Dreamin' Surf 'N Shop	25	☐	☐
Little Theatre	500	☐	☐	California Dreamin' Beach Taxi	25	☐	☐
Little Theatre Story Boards (3)	35	☐	☐	California Dreamin' Hot Dog Stand	40	☐	☐
BARBIE® Goes To College	330	☐	☐	Six O'Clock News	35	☐	☐
BARBIE® and Skipper® School	350	☐	☐	Step 'N Style Boutique	35	☐	☐
Fashion Stage	75	☐	☐	Hollywood Hair Beauty Center	15	☐	☐
BARBIE® Cafe Today	125	☐	☐	BARBIE® Supermarket	25	☐	☐
Olympic Ski Village	50	☐	☐	Baby Care Center	10	☐	☐
Fashion Plaza	115	☐	☐	Post Office	15	☐	☐
Sweetheart Park	95	☐	☐	Magic Moves Home Office	15	☐	☐
SuperStar Photo Studio	75	☐	☐	All-American Hamburger Stand	35	☐	☐
Reservation Center	25	☐	☐	Tracey Bride doll	40	☐	☐
Play Pak				Todd Groom doll	40	☐	☐
Get Aways	30	☐	☐	California Dreamin' dolls			
Campin' Out	30	☐	☐	BARBIE®	75	☐	☐
Western Round Up	25	☐	☐	Ken®	65	☐	☐
Horseback Riding	25	☐	☐	Skipper® – Available only in Germany	175	☐	☐
Tracy & Todd Wedding	40	☐	☐	Midge®	55	☐	☐
Dream Store – Fashion Department	55	☐	☐	Christie®	55	☐	☐
Dream Store – Make-Up Department	45	☐	☐	Teresa	55	☐	☐
Great Shape Workout Center	40	☐	☐	BARBIE® Pretty Treasures	5 each	☐	☐
Dinner Date	35	☐	☐	Hot Skatin' BARBIE® doll 2-in-1 Skatin' Fun	14	☐	☐
BARBIE® Island Fun Hut	50	☐	☐	BARBIE® Picnic Set	12	☐	☐

Chapter 11 – The Pet Menagerie

Item	Price	I Have	I Want	Item	Price	I Have	I Want
Dancer	$60	☐	☐	Blinking Beauty	25	☐	☐
Dallas	35	☐	☐	Zizi	25	☐	☐
Midnight	35	☐	☐	Ginger	25	☐	☐
Honey - pony	25	☐	☐	Vet Fun Fashion Playset	85	☐	☐
Dixie	20	☐	☐	BARBIE® Pretty Pet Parlor	10	☐	☐
Fluff	45	☐	☐	High Stepper Horse	30	☐	☐
Beauty	30	☐	☐	Puppy Ruff	10	☐	☐
Beauty and Puppies	40	☐	☐	Mitzi Meow	10	☐	☐
Prince	25	☐	☐				
Tahiti	25	☐	☐				

Chapter 12 – THE TOY CHEST

	I Have	I Want
View-Master Reels		
Sawyer's – BARBIE®'s Around The World Trip ..$125	☐	☐
GAF – BARBIE® Around the World Trip 100	☐	☐
GAF – BARBIE® Great American Photo Race 100	☐	☐
GAF – Talking View-Master 100	☐	☐
GAF – Talking View-Master – BARBIE®'s Around The World Trip 250	☐	☐
GAF – Talking View Master – BARBIE®'s Great American Photo Race 150	☐	☐
GAF – SuperStar BARBIE®, 1978 18	☐	☐
View-Master – BARBIE® and The Rockers 15	☐	☐
View-Master – BARBIE® and The Rockers Go On Tour Gift Set 25	☐	☐
View-Master – BARBIE®/Featuring SuperStar BARBIE®, 1989...10	☐	☐
ColorForms		
BARBIE® Dress-Up Kit, 1970 40	☐	☐
BARBIE® Dress-Up Kits; various editions ......10 each	☐	☐

	I Have	I Want
The BARBIE® Dream House Playset 25	☐	☐
BARBIE® Dress-Up Sets Travel Paks ....6 each	☐	☐
"Hanes makes Ken® feel good all under" 25	☐	☐
Farrow Industries Miniatures ....5 to 12 each	☐	☐
Forever BARBIE® Miniature Collectibles ....20 each	☐	☐
Miniature BARBIE® Collectibles ....18 each	☐	☐
Applause		
'BARBIE® Style' BARBIE® doll 75	☐	☐
2nd Edition BARBIE® doll 65	☐	☐
Figurines ....5 each	☐	☐
Figurine Key Rings ....8 each	☐	☐
Pencils ....4 each	☐	☐
"Dance! Workout with BARBIE®" video.....................16	☐	☐
Notebook Transfers 3	☐	☐
Flying BARBIE® Disc 5	☐	☐
BARBIE® YoYo 5	☐	☐
BARBIE® Hula Hoop 12	☐	☐
Sky Master Kite 5	☐	☐

Chapter 13 – CREATIVITY – SEWING, KNITTING, AND ARTS & CRAFTS

	I Have	I Want
Knitting for BARBIE®...................................$45	☐	☐
Color By Number 65	☐	☐
Electric Drawing Set 60	☐	☐
Fashion Embroidery Set...............................100	☐	☐
1960's Patterns 10	☐	☐
Sew-Free Fashion Patterns 75	☐	☐
1963, McCall's Pattern Advertisement 12	☐	☐
1983, Shrinky Dinks Set 8	☐	☐

	I Have	I Want
Sewing Cards 5	☐	☐
BARBIE® Rub and Color 10	☐	☐
Glitter Paint By Number 3	☐	☐
Fashion Decorator System 8	☐	☐
Jewelry Holder 8	☐	☐
Rub and Color 10	☐	☐
BARBIE® Sand Fun 5	☐	☐

Chapter 14 – FUN ACTIVITIES

	I Have	I Want
BARBIE® and Ken® 1962 Coloring Book (uncolored) $35	☐	☐
BARBIE® and Ken® 1963 Jigsaw Puzzle 50	☐	☐
Dynamic Toy Co. Trading Cards ....12 each	☐	☐
Whitman Publishing Co. Coloring Books ....15 each	☐	☐
Whitman Publishing Co. Coloring Books with Paper Dolls ....20 each	☐	☐
Golden Coloring Books ....10 each	☐	☐
ColorForms BARBIE® Color and Play 12	☐	☐
1982, Trading Cards..2 each	☐	☐
1982, Whitman – Jigsaw Puzzles 20	☐	☐
Whitman Frame-Tray-Puzzles 25	☐	☐
Golden Frame-Tray-Puzzles..10	☐	☐
Golden BARBIE® Crayons...5	☐	☐
Large Coloring Books – Merrigold Press 12	☐	☐
Sticker Decals ....4 each	☐	☐

	I Have	I Want
Hoyle Products – 1985 Sticker Calendar 18	☐	☐
Golden Activity Books...5	☐	☐
BARBIE® Diary 18	☐	☐
1989, Nostalgic BARBIE® 550 Piece Jigsaw Puzzle......25	☐	☐
1990, BARBIE® Trading Cards ....1 each	☐	☐
1990, BARBIE® Trading Cards Deluxe Set 90	☐	☐
1990, BARBIE® Trading Cards Poster............................25	☐	☐
BARBIE® Memories Scrapbook 22	☐	☐
BARBIE® Fashion Color & Play 12	☐	☐
Golden Miniature – BARBIE® Fun Book 6	☐	☐
Glitter Star 110 Camera 10	☐	☐
Growth Chart 20	☐	☐
Fun Camera 15	☐	☐
Stamper Sets ....5 each	☐	☐

Chapter 15 – DINING WITH BARBIE® DOLL

	I Have	I Want
Worchester – Tea Services $75	☐	☐
Worchester – Dishes 75	☐	☐
Irwin – BARBIE® Heirloom Service Playset 80	☐	☐
Thermos Lunch Box with Thermos Bottle.........95 to 140	☐	☐

	I Have	I Want
Thermos Bottles 35	☐	☐
Lunch Boxes...50	☐	☐
BARBIE® Loves McDonald®'s Restaurant....................100	☐	☐
Fun At McDonald®'s Uniforms 45	☐	☐

	I Have	I Want
Chilton-Globe – Genuine BARBIE® Party Sets 30	☐	☐
"The BARBIE® Party Cookbook" 15	☐	☐
Wilton Enterprises – Cake Pan 12	☐	☐
Little Debbie Snack Cakes BARBIE® doll with Mail-in Offers 60	☐	☐
Pizza Party! Skipper®'s Pizza Shop 10	☐	☐
1991 McDonald®'s Display with Translites 450	☐	☐
1991 McDonald®'s Display without Translites 275	☐	☐
1991 McDonald®'s Happy Meal™ BARBIE® Set of 8 Figurines w/boxes 160	☐	☐
1991 McDonald®'s Happy Meal™ BARBIE® Figurines ......10 each	☐	☐
1991 McDonald®'s Happy Meal™ BARBIE® Boxes ..10 each	☐	☐
1992 McDonald®'s Display 190	☐	☐
1992 McDonald®'s Happy Meal™ BARBIE® Set of 8 Figurines w/boxes...................120	☐	☐
1992 McDonald®'s Happy Meal™ BARBIE® Figurines ..5 each	☐	☐
1992 McDonald®'s Happy Meal™ BARBIE® Boxes ..10 each	☐	☐

	I Have	I Want
1993 McDonald®'s Display 160	☐	☐
1993 McDonald®'s Translite 25	☐	☐
1993 McDonald®'s Happy Meal™ BARBIE® Set of 8 Figurines w/sacks 60	☐	☐
1993 McDonald®'s Happy Meal™ BARBIE® Figurines ..4 each	☐	☐
1993 McDonald®'s Happy Meal™ BARBIE® Sacks....3 each	☐	☐
1994 McDonald®'s Display 125	☐	☐
1994 McDonald®'s Happy Meal™ BARBIE® Set of 8 Figurines w/sacks 60	☐	☐
1994 McDonald®'s Happy Meal™ BARBIE® Figurines ..4 each	☐	☐
1994 McDonald®'s Happy Meal™ BARBIE® Sacks..3 each	☐	☐
1994 McDonald®'s Happy Meal™ African American Locket Surprise pair.............30	☐	☐
1994 McDonald®'s Tray Line 15	☐	☐
1995 McDonald®'s Display 125	☐	☐
BARBIE® & Ken® Chefs Salt and Pepper Shakers......40	☐	☐
Enchanted Evening Cake Figurine...................6	☐	☐

Chapter 16 – TOUCHES OF BARBIE® DOLL GLAMOUR

	I Have	I Want
BARBIE®'s Wig Wardrobe.........................$175	☐	☐
Bradley Time Watches ....50 to 225	☐	☐
SuperStar BARBIE® Fur & Jewels Safe 25	☐	☐
Perfume Pretty BARBIE® Gift For Two 15	☐	☐
DuCair Bioessence Products....................3 to 12	☐	☐
DuCair Bioessence – BARBIE® Cologne with a Pink Bear......20	☐	☐
Cannon Wash Cloth 5	☐	☐
Peter Brams Designs		
Sterling Silver Charm Bracelet.............295	☐	☐
18-Karat Gold Plated Charm Bracelet 100	☐	☐
Avon BARBIE® Jewelry..........................8	☐	☐
Nostalgic BARBIE® Ceramic Pin 15	☐	☐
BARBIE® Musical Jewelry Box.....................20	☐	☐
BARBIE® For Girls		
Hair Bows 5	☐	☐
Adhesive Bandages 5	☐	☐
Cosmetic Set 8	☐	☐
Book Bag 15	☐	☐
Jewelry Box 10	☐	☐

	I Have	I Want
FAO Schwarz – BARBIE® On Madison Watch 65	☐	☐
Hope Industries BARBIE® For Girls Watches 15	☐	☐
Masquerade Ball BARBIE® doll		
with Mackie Perfume 895	☐	☐
without the Perfume 750	☐	☐
Fossil Watches 1994, editions ....130 each	☐	☐
Nicole Miller Nostalgic BARBIE® Scarf.....................175	☐	☐
Nicole Miller – Bloomingdales Savy Shopper BARBIE® doll......250	☐	☐
Make Me Pretty BARBIE® Head 18	☐	☐
Evans Furs – Lazarus Department Store, BARBIE® in Mink......275	☐	☐
Designs From The Deep FAO Schwarz 2 mirror compact 40	☐	☐
Bloomingdale's Donna Karan New York BARBIE® doll 150	☐	☐
Fossil Watches "Solo In the Spotlight" Sterling Silver in Black Grand Piano...........400	☐	☐
Pink Grand Piano 100	☐	☐

Chapter 17 – CALENDARS, BIRTHDAYS, AND HOLIDAYS

	I Have	I Want
Flourish Gift Wrap $5	☐	☐
Hallmark – Happy Birthday from BARBIE® plates 10	☐	☐
BARBIE® Wrap-An-Egg Decorating Kit.........................8	☐	☐
Gibson Wrapping Paper		
Package of single sheet...............................10	☐	☐
Roll 5	☐	☐
Gibson Greeting Cards		
Paper Dolls 10	☐	☐
Puzzles 8	☐	☐
Various Cards 5	☐	☐
Unique Industries Birthday Ensemble.....................6 each	☐	☐
Unique Industries Birthday Candle 10	☐	☐
Cleo – Children's Valentines 5	☐	☐

	I Have	I Want
Nostalgic Calendars ....18 each	☐	☐
Nostalgic BARBIE® Postcard Book...........................15	☐	☐
Forever BARBIE® Postcard Book 15	☐	☐
Gibson – Gift Bags 3	☐	☐
BARBIE® Party Time 15	☐	☐
Hallmark Cards – Glamour Dream Collection 40	☐	☐
Hallmark Greeting Cards 3	☐	☐
1995 Hallmark Calendar 10	☐	☐
Hallmark Birthday Ensemble ....3 to 8	☐	☐
Hallmark Wrapping Paper 2	☐	☐
Hallmark Gift Card 1	☐	☐
Ambassador Gift Wrap...........................2	☐	☐
Mattel, Inc. Greeting Fashion Cards 3	☐	☐

	I Have	I Want
McDonald®'s – Happy Birthday Special Guest BARBIE® ..25	☐	☐
Hallmark Keepsake Ornaments		
Holiday BARBIE® #1 150	☐	☐
Holiday BARBIE® #2 100	☐	☐
Holiday BARBIE® #3 35	☐	☐
Debut 1959 BARBIE® 100	☐	☐
Solo In The Spotlight 45	☐	☐
Springtime BARBIE® #1 45	☐	☐
Hallmark Displays		
1993 Counter Top Promotional 20	☐	☐

	I Have	I Want
Debut 1959 BARBIE® Promotional Sign 15	☐	☐
1994 Happy Holiday BARBIE® Ornament Display ..15	☐	☐
1995 Solo In The Spotlight Display 25	☐	☐
Fashion Greeting Card – Happy Holidays 3	☐	☐
Ambassador Greeting Card 3	☐	☐
Victorian Elegance BARBIE® doll 250	☐	☐
Holiday Memories BARBIE® doll 135	☐	☐
1995 Hallmark Children's Valentines 5	☐	☐

Chapter 18 – MATTEL, INC.'S PROMOTIONS AND PREMIUMS

	I Have	I Want
1976 BARBIE® World of Fashion Calendar $100	☐	☐
Mattel, Inc. BARBIE® License Book 15	☐	☐
Mattel, Inc. Wish List Booklets 5	☐	☐
BARBIE® Fashions 1983 Store Display 250	☐	☐
BARBIE® Fashions Display Boxes 15	☐	☐
BARBIE® Fashion Center Shelf Strip 10	☐	☐
I'm Into BARBIE® Shelf Strip 10	☐	☐
Jewel Secrets Store Display 550	☐	☐
BARBIE® Le Nouveau Theatre De La Mode signed		
by Billy Boy w/booklets 600	☐	☐
Feelin' Groovy BARBIE® doll 300	☐	☐
BARBIE® On Tour Poster 50	☐	☐
Mattel, Inc. Catalogues 25	☐	☐
Department Store Special Catalogues 20	☐	☐
Timeless Creations Catalogues 15	☐	☐
Pink Jubilee 30 Magical Years Display Sign 40	☐	☐

	I Have	I Want
Toy Club		
BARBIE® Fan On Board Sign 10	☐	☐
Toy Club 35th Anniversary BARBIE® Pin 35	☐	☐
35th Anniversary Brunette BARBIE® doll 900	☐	☐
Summit BARBIE® Display 25	☐	☐
Sneak Preview 1991 Calendar 25	☐	☐
BARBIE® 1991 Line Promotional Book 30	☐	☐
1991 Store Display Pictures 30	☐	☐
BARBIE® Fashion Secrets Video 20	☐	☐
BARBIE® Magazine – 35th Anniversary Issue		
for Retailers 35	☐	☐
Stock Quarterly Report 5	☐	☐
Annual Report 10	☐	☐
Mattel, Inc. Stock Certificates with		
Ruth Handler's signature ....20 each	☐	☐
Palmolive Soap – Tutti® Mail-in offer 15	☐	☐

Chapter 19 – COMMEMORATIVE MERCHANDISE

	I Have	I Want
25th Anniversary China Service		
with certificate and hanging tag $200	☐	☐
without certificate and hanging tag 65	☐	☐
30th Anniversary Commemorative Medallion		
1 oz. pure silver 250	☐	☐
silver-plated 50	☐	☐
30th Anniversary Poster 75	☐	☐
Danbury Mint – High Fashion Plates set of 8 ....250 set	☐	☐
Chilton Globe 35th China Service 40	☐	☐
35th Anniversary BARBIE® Festival		
Banquet Dolls (Blonde and Titian) 2,000	☐	☐
Tote Bag 45	☐	☐
35th Anniversary Festival BARBIE® doll 500	☐	☐

	I Have	I Want
Nostalgic 35th Anniversary Gift Set 1,000	☐	☐
Nostalgic 35th Anniversary Gift Set signed by		
Ruth Handler 1,800	☐	☐
1962, Ruth Handler and Elliot Handler Photograph 300	☐	☐
Official Festival Souvenir Pin 75	☐	☐
Key Ring 10	☐	☐
Cap 25	☐	☐
Autograph Card signed by Ruth Handler 100	☐	☐
Dream Doll, The Ruth Handler Story signed autobiography ..135	☐	☐
"BARBIE® is the Number 1 Doll" advertisement 25	☐	☐
Silver Anniversary edition "BARBIE® Through The Years" 25	☐	☐
Christian Dior BARBIE® doll 200	☐	☐

Chapter 20 – GLOBAL DOLLS AND ACCESSORIES

	I Have	I Want
German Patio Furniture $60	☐	☐
BARBIE® Hundesede (dog sled) 350	☐	☐
Dream Carriage 250	☐	☐
Winter-Garden 400	☐	☐
Takara-Kimono BARBIE® doll 115	☐	☐
Takara-Ken® doll 115	☐	☐
"Journal BARBIE®" German Fan Club Publications 5	☐	☐
"Vogue-France" 18	☐	☐
Rose Du Soir/Festival Rosa BARBIE® doll 120	☐	☐

	I Have	I Want
BARBIE® Feliz Aniversario doll 150	☐	☐
Calgary Olympic Winter Games – Skating Star		
BARBIE®-doll 100	☐	☐
Freundschafts-Berlin Wall Commemorative for the		
Reunification of Germany, 1990 BARBIE® doll 125	☐	☐
Action-Banini Trading Cards ....2 each	☐	☐
Dancing Cinderella BARBIE® doll 175	☐	☐
Korean BARBIE® doll 95	☐	☐
Champion Horse 40	☐	☐